THE WORLD OF THE GREAT HORNED OWL

A LIVING WORLD BOOK
John K. Terres, Editor

LIVING WORLD BOOKS
John K. Terres, Editor

The World of the Ant by David F. Costello

The World of the Beaver by Leonard Lee Rue III

The World of the Black Bear by Joe Van Wormer

The World of the Bobcat by Joe Van Wormer

The World of the Canada Goose by Joe Van Wormer

The World of the Coyote by Joe Van Wormer

The World of the Frog and the Toad by George Porter

The World of the Great Horned Owl
   by G. Ronald Austing and John B. Holt, Jr.

The World of the Grizzly Bear by W. J. Schoonmaker

The World of the Opossum by James F. Keefe
   with photographs by Don Wooldridge

The World of the Porcupine by David F. Costello

The World of the Pronghorn by Joe Van Wormer

The World of the Raccoon by Leonard Lee Rue III

The World of the Red Fox by Leonard Lee Rue III

The World of the Red-tailed Hawk by G. Ronald Austing

The World of the White-tailed Deer by Leonard Lee Rue III

The World of the Wolf by Russell J. Rutter and
   Douglas H. Pimlott

The World of the Woodchuck by W. J. Schoonmaker

THE WORLD OF

THE GREAT HORNED OWL

TEXT AND PHOTOGRAPHS BY

G. RONALD AUSTING AND JOHN B. HOLT, JR.

J. B. LIPPINCOTT COMPANY

PHILADELPHIA & NEW YORK

To our parents

CONTENTS

The World of the Great Horned Owl

THE OWL ITSELF

We human beings are essentially diurnal creatures, but this is not true of many of the birds and animals that inhabit this planet with us. As the sun sinks low on the horizon and the long shadows of evening creep through the woods, various mice, rabbits, raccoons, opossums, flying squirrels, deer, and other creatures emerge from their daytime concealment and begin their nightly forays.

In this world of darkness, predatory birds and mammals are also on the prowl, assuring that nature's intricate system of checks and balances shall not be disrupted and that no essential job—for example, curbing the rodent hordes—is left undone. Chief among these nocturnal predators is a specialized order of birds called Strigiformes, the owls, which are characterized by extraordinary powers of vision, together with a soft downy plumage enabling practically soundless flight. If hawks, in their function of keeping within bounds the populations of mammals and birds, are on the "day shift," owls may be said to be on the "night shift."

Perhaps the most outstanding and controversial member of this tribe of night flyers is the celebrated "Tiger of the Air," the great horned owl, *Bubo virginianus*. Often described as the fiercest and most savage of all predatory birds, it has been shot, trapped, and discriminated against for years throughout its wide range, by farmers, sportsmen, gamekeepers, and even some naturalists, but it continues to survive as one of our commonest large owls.

The great horned owl is the classic representative of a "hoot owl"

13

Portrait of an adult male horned owl

to the layman, for its low, melancholy—often booming—notes are probably more familiar than the voices of any other of the eighteen species of North American owls. Moreover, it is most often the bird that people envision whenever the expression "wise old owl" is used: the owl's flat, feathered facial disks and wide-set eyes give it an almost human expression, and the presence of "ear" tufts (from which the bird gets its name) tends to increase its scholarly appearance and magnificent bearing.

The great horned owl is one of our largest owls, measuring 18 to 25 inches in length and with a wingspread of more than four feet. It weighs about three pounds and is comparable in size and weight to the snowy owl of the subarctic tundra regions. Only the great gray owl of the Canadian wilderness surpasses it in over-all length and wingspread: this bird, however, is deceptive in appearance, having long wings and tail, a large round head, and long fluffy plumage. These give the great gray owl an appearance of immense size, but in weight and actual body measurements it is exceeded by both the snowy owl and the great horned owl, both of which are substantially more powerful birds, capable of killing larger animals.

At the approach of dawn, most owls seek seclusion in densely foliated trees, vines, or hollows; since they seldom expose themselves by day, many people believe that they cannot see in daylight. But the eyes of an owl are among the most remarkable in the bird world: in darkness the pupils can be dilated almost as wide as the eye itself, giving the retina access to as much light as possible. As light intensity increases, a gradual contraction of the pupils allows just the right amount to reach the retina and form the image, and in very bright light the pupil becomes so small that it appears as a mere dark speck in the yellow iris.

In addition to this unique quality, the retina—that part of the eye which receives the image and transfers it to the central nervous system—has special adaptations for nocturnal vision. It contains rod-shaped receptor cells, effective in gathering light, and cone-shaped receptor cells, which function in bright light and play a major role in color vision. While diurnal birds have a great abundance of cone-shaped cells but comparatively few rods, the owls have many more rods than cones. This gives them superior vision in poor light but at the same time renders them more or less color-blind. They see most images in various shades of gray, black, and white.

The eyes of most birds (songbirds are a good example) are located on each side of the head, giving them a wide field of monocular vision to either side and a limited range of binocular vision directly in front, where there is an overlap of each eye's field of view. The eyes of an owl are situated on the front of a relatively flat face, giving it a wider range of binocular vision than any other bird.

Binocular vision gives the three-dimensional effect necessary for distance determination; it is vital to hawks and owls, which hunt living prey and must be able to judge distances accurately and quickly. Though a desirable trait, it is greatly exaggerated in the owl family and tends to reduce their over-all visual field. An owl sees only what is directly in front of it and must rotate its head to take full account of its surroundings. Because its eyes are set so wide apart and the eyeballs themselves are so rigidly fixed in the sockets, an owl has difficulty focusing at close range and often backs away from near objects in order to see them clearly.

Owls also have the unique ability to drop the top eyelid when blinking, but they raise the lower eyelid when sleeping just as other birds do. Also, like all other birds, they have a transparent nictitating membrane, sometimes referred to as a "third eyelid." It is controlled by involuntary reflex action, and its primary function is to cleanse the eyes and keep them moist.

The ears of an owl, under the feathers of the skull, are long asymmetrical slits located behind the facial disks on either side of the head. They are an essential part of the bird's sensory apparatus, playing as important a role in the detection of prey at night as does vision itself. Experiments conducted by Roger S. Payne of the New York State

Portrait of an adult male snowy owl, a species equal in size to the horned owl

Close-up of a young horned owl, showing contracted irises

Close-up of a snowy owl, showing how the eyelids work to reduce intense light.

College of Agriculture seem to have proved that owls are capable of locating prey entirely by sound. Payne placed a captive barn owl in a totally darkened room, the floor of which had been covered with dried leaves. When Payne released live mice in the dark room, the owl caught them without difficulty. Thinking the mouse's body temperature might possibly be aiding in its detection, Payne repeated the experiment, this time dragging a wad of paper through the leaves with a string. The owl struck the paper with high accuracy, leading Payne to conclude that sound alone had guided the bird to its target.

Further tests by Payne indicated that the owl's accuracy depends to some extent on the sound frequency or number of aerial vibrations produced per second. The bird's eardrums were found to be highly directional for sound frequencies over 9,000 cycles per second.

Payne suggests that the owl locates its prey by turning its head until the intensity of all vibrations producing the sound are at a maximum in both ears, at which time it is automatically facing the sound source.

Although Payne's experiments involved only the barn owl, the conclusions of his experiments seem applicable to owls in general, perhaps with some variations between different species.

18

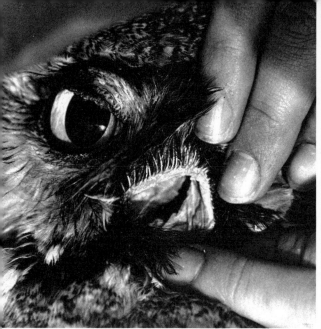

Close-up of a horned owl's ear

A young barn owl, nearly fledged, almost identical to an adult

Owls are not usually credited with a highly developed sense of smell, but information pertaining to this subject is contradictory and unsubstantiated. A Canadian author, Farley Mowat, who apparently kept two horned owls for some length of time, claimed that the scent of skunk on the night air would transform one of his birds into a feathered terror, so great was its anticipation of a feast. Though horned owls occasionally dine on skunk, it is not likely that they normally hunt these animals by scent.

Most owls hunt at night or in the subdued light of late evening or early dawn. When environmental conditions prevent this, however, they adapt quite readily. This trait is best illustrated by certain species of northern owls, including the snowy owl, the short-eared owl, and the hawk owl. Since periods of darkness are short during the summer months, these birds adopt more or less diurnal habits at this time. Summer is also the time of greatest activity in the reproductive cycle. During the dark winter months, they revert to a more completely nocturnal existence again.

19

Short-eared owl

Although the Arctic horned owl and other subspecies might well fit into the category of partially diurnal owls, the great horned owl of the temperate zones is pre-eminently a bird of the night. However, it too will occasionally hunt by day when hard pressed for food, especially on dark, cloudy days during the winter.

Most great horned owls tend to live in the same general vicinity more or less continuously throughout the year; this is called maintaining a permanent home range. Simply defined, the home range of a bird or other animal is a portion of land or water fulfilling the biological requirements of the species. For a horned owl, such a place must contain suitable nesting sites for raising its young, roosting cover for daytime concealment, and fairly open hunting territory. Above all, the home range must support enough wildlife to provide an adequate, annual food supply for the owl and its family.

The size of the home range seems to depend largely on the type of habitat and the available food supply. In the West and Midwest, where horned owl prey is more abundant, ranges of horned owls are often quite small, a square mile or less being sufficient in many cases. But in the East, where food is not so plentiful, the owls must hunt over a larger area to satisfy their needs. Undoubtedly the home ranges of

20

Pitch-pine and scrub-oak habitat (Cape Cod, Mass.)

some eastern great horned owls are considerably larger than is generally supposed, probably as much as two or three square miles.

Pairs of great horned owls maintaining large home ranges usually confine most of their activities to a fairly limited portion of that range for one or two seasons at a time. Then they move on to other parts for comparable periods until, finally, they return to the initial tract after a lapse of several years. Accordingly, they may appear to be impermanent residents in an area. From their absences, a casual observer might well conclude that the original pair of owls had deserted the area altogether, to be later replaced by a second pair. Actually, the same birds may have been present all the time in some distant part of their large range.

The size of the habitat ranged over by a pair of great horned owls is governed also by topography, distribution and types of plant life, and other environmental conditions. Normally the home range of a pair of owls will include a rather large woodland area together with adjacent fields and smaller wood lots. There the birds will carry on their life functions until death severs the pair-bond which unites them. In this event the survivor usually occupies the same territory until a new mate

21

happens along. Eventually both original birds may be replaced in this way, but generally there is at least one bird associated with the home range, holding it until a new mate is secured and then continuing to occupy it.

Defense of the home range is subject to considerable variation: it is affected not only by the same factors which govern the size and extent of the range itself but also by the seasonal changes in the temperaments of the birds themselves. As a general rule, a pair of horned owls will keep their range clear of individuals of their kind; however, they frequently permit other birds of prey to establish ranges within their territory's invisible boundaries. Such tolerance is often greatly heightened in areas where prey is abundant and where most hawk and owl ranges are correspondingly small. A great abundance of prey—mice or rats or rabbits, for example—usually results in the overlapping of ranges and territories of many owls and hawks, even of the same species. Under such conditions, each pair may actively defend only a very small portion of the over-all range.

Within the home range, great horned owls have favorite nesting and roosting areas which they use with great regularity from year to year. Some birds adhere so rigorously to a seasonal roosting routine that it is sometimes possible to predict even the exact trees in which they may be found at certain times of the year. This is particularly true when dense cover is scarce, or during the fall and winter, when deciduous trees are bare. These factors reduce the number of places in which a bird as large as a great horned owl can find suitable cover. At such times coniferous needle-bearing trees are favored over all other locations. In the absence of pines, hemlocks, spruces, or other conifers, the owls must find seclusion elsewhere. This may be in certain deciduous trees, such as oaks and beeches, some of which tend to hold clusters of dried leaves throughout the winter; in vine tangles or under broken limbs hanging against the side of a tree; or they may simply perch on a small horizontal branch on the trunk of a sizable tree. Great horned

The Owl Itself

Male horned owl with a Norway rat

owls may seek shelter in just about any place that offers them concealment or at least tends to make them as inconspicuous as possible in their surroundings.

In northeastern Massachusetts, pines, spruces, and hemlocks are fairly common in most woodlands; even stands of predominantly deciduous trees are usually interspersed with some conifers. With such a number of preferred roosting sites available, it is interesting to note some of the peculiar hiding or roosting places which seem to strike the fancy of many eastern great horned owls. Several specific examples from our own experience illustrate this: a small group of white pines in a red maple swamp, set apart from an extensive hillside stand of pines; the largest white pine in a white-pine grove; the smallest white pine in a similar grove; a lone hemlock tree in a white pine stand; an isolated white pine in a red-pine plantation; a single white pine surrounded by

A roost grove of white pines (North Andover, Mass.)

pitch pines; and a solitary pitch pine in a grove of white pines and
hemlocks.

In each of the foregoing examples, the roost tree itself had certain
characteristics that tended to distinguish it from the surrounding
growth. Not all great horned owls are quite so fastidious in their
selection, but there is a strong tendency for them to be attracted to
roost trees which are more or less segregated, either by size, type, or
location. It almost seems as though the birds do so in an effort to make
it easier for them to identify their individual roosting trees.

The great horned owl and the red-tailed hawk are usually considered complementary species. Each hunts similar prey over the same

24

A vine tangle, typical Ohio roost of horned owls in winter

type of habitat, one by night, the other by day. Each is essentially a woodland as well as an open-country bird. Physically each has long broad wings and a short tail. Great horned owls and red-tailed hawks of the eastern United States usually prefer substantial tracts of heavy timber for nesting and seclusion, but in the Far West more open country is commonly used by both species. Both are generally birds of dry upland country, whether it is the hilly and mountainous regions in the East, the flat well-drained farmlands of the Midwest, or the deserts of the Southwest.

A similar complementary relationship seems to exist between the red-shouldered hawk and the barred owl. Both are primarily woodland

25

A white pine roost tree

A nest site in a red cedar (southern Ohio)

species, with shorter wings and longer tails in relation to their body length than open-country hawks and owls; they often live quite harmoniously together in the same woods and normally occupy swampy

26

woodlands, river bottoms, and wet, wooded lowlands throughout the country.

In contrast is northeastern Massachusetts, where the topography of the land is generally low and swampy, but the nesting population of large predatory birds consists predominantly of the red-shouldered hawk and the great horned owl. In this region, however, the association of these two species is far from a close one. The owls tend to occupy tracts of mature white pine trees, and they range only slightly into the surrounding deciduous woods. The hawks, on the other hand, usually occupy extensive deciduous swamps as far removed from any great horned owl range as possible. As a result, the paths of the two birds seldom cross; but should a red-shoulder return in the spring to find its nest of the previous season taken over by horned owls, it often refuses to nest under such disturbing circumstances, being unable to adjust to the owl's sudden invasion of its former domain.

Biologists classify the great horned owl as a general feeder, which means that it is large enough, strong enough, and fast enough to capture just about any animal it fancies as prey. It can therefore alter its diet in accord with those populations that live within its range, shifting from one animal to another as fluctuations in density and availability of prey make this necessary. This helps the owl to remain more or less sedentary throughout the year, whereas other birds of prey with more restricted feeding habits are often forced to move elsewhere as seasonal declines in certain animal populations occur.

Few creatures of the field and forest entirely escape the attacks of the great horned owl, as indicated by the long list of animals it is known to prey upon. These include a great variety of mammals, ranging in size from rabbits, squirrels, skunks, woodchucks, and domestic cats to the smaller rats, mice, shrews, and bats; and of birds from the larger geese, ducks, chickens, herons, crows, and hawks down to the smaller starlings, juncos, and other sparrow-sized species. In addition to these, the great horned owl eats snakes, fishes, crayfish, insects, and scorpions.

Horned owl prey:

    porcupine (photo by Karl H. Maslowski)

    striped skunk (photo by Karl H. Maslowski)

    flying squirrel (photo by Karl H. Maslowski)

    cottontail (photo by Austing and Koehler)

The World of the Great Horned Owl

The impressive list of birds and animals the horned owl is known to eat speaks well for its prowess and skill in capturing and killing its prey. However, this variety of foods should not suggest that horned owls normally feed on all or even most of the species mentioned. Generally they prefer small to medium-sized animals, with mice, rabbits and other rodents being recorded most often in their stomachs or regurgitated pellets. Under stress of hunger, however, or when other kinds of food are especially abundant and available, the owl may feed on surprisingly larger or even smaller prey than usual.

Records of horned owls seizing such formidable opponents as skunks, house cats, and porcupines are not uncommon, but animals of this size and caliber are usually attacked only when the bird is hard pressed for food. The dried skins of horned owls in museums sometimes smell strongly of skunk, and observations seem to indicate that the owl has little or no trouble in subduing these creatures despite their defensive spray. Domestic cats, on the other hand, frequently fight back so fiercely that the owl must sometimes release them from its powerful grasp. A battle with a porcupine can bring disaster to either or both contestants; a horned owl has been found dead with porcupine quills sprinkled liberally throughout its body.

Another dangerous prey for the great horned owl is the blacksnake. At least two experiences have been noted by naturalists in which an owl has seized one of these reptiles, only to have the snake retaliate by coiling itself so tightly around the owl's body that in both cases the owl was near exhaustion when discovered. Had it not been for human intervention, the tide of battle could have gone in either direction.

To a considerable extent the great horned owl preys by opportunity, taking what is most readily available and easily procured; this habit is shared by most animals that are considered omnivorous or general feeders. For this reason it is difficult or impossible to evaluate the feeding habits of the owl in different parts of the country. Their

30

prey—its type and the numbers taken—will depend largely on locality, availability, and season of the year.

Generally, as certain animals such as rodents, cottontail rabbits, and others reach population peaks, their vulnerability to predation also increases, and they will experience greater losses to natural enemies than less populous prey or prey with smaller population densities. Because of the universal abundance and prolific nature of rodents and other small mammals, it is not surprising to find that they are basic items in the horned owl's diet. Detailed food-habit studies of great horned owls have shown that in some localities as much as 90 per cent of their winter diet is composed of several species of rats and mice; rabbits, too, are staple items at this time of the year.

When food is plentiful, the owl will sometimes become so fastidious that it will consume only the choicest portions of the animals it has killed and will discard the rest. E. O. Niles tells of a nest of great horned owls containing two young birds and several dead rats. On the ground below the nest were the bodies of 113 rats, recently killed, with their skulls open and brains removed. Apparently this part of the animal is considered a delicacy by the bird.

In our studies of the great horned owl, we found that not all individuals help man's economy by subsisting entirely on the kinds of wildlife that compete with man for his food. Where poultry or game birds are easily obtained, the owl is quite naturally inclined to take full advantage of their availability. It will often continue its raids on poultry, especially on open range, until it is finally killed by an irate farmer or gamekeeper. We cannot, however, condemn the entire species because some occasionally kill pen-reared domestic poultry or those pheasants destined for release on game lands. The fault is often that of the poultryman or gamekeeper who makes his birds easily available to owls and other predators. The owl is an important and necessary part of any healthy wildlife community and should be recognized as such. Sometimes local control measures may be unavoidable, but a campaign of wholesale extermination is not the answer to greater poultry or game yields and will ultimately result in far greater economic loss than the damage these owls may be capable of causing to poultry and pen-raised game birds.

When devouring its prey, the great horned owl usually begins at the head and eats backward. Birds are plucked, but small mammals such as mice and rats are swallowed whole, headfirst; and even when larger kills are torn apart, the owl still consumes variable quantities of bones, fur, and feathers along with edible portions. Such indigestible substances do not pass through the stomach but, instead, are regurgitated as *castings* through the mouth in the form of a pellet, two to four inches in length (unbroken), and an inch and a half or so in diameter. Since most of these castings occur before the owl leaves its roost on the day following a meal, the ground beneath the regular roosting tree is usually littered with them, along with white splashes of excrement (often called "whitewash") from the roosting birds.

Signs of this sort are easily overlooked in the woods unless one has a fairly good idea of what to look for and where to find it. They are invaluable aids to the research biologist, not only as a means of detecting the presence of owls and tracing their seasonal movements but also as a way of studying their feeding habits directly through pellet analysis —just about everything an owl eats will be represented in pellet samples from the bird.

Unlike the wavering, mothlike flight of most of the smaller owls, the flight of the great horned owl is powerful, swift, and unfaltering. When disturbed in the daytime, it usually departs from its roosting tree on a downward plane with several strong pumps of its broad wings until sufficient momentum is gathered to carry it along on set wings at no great distance from the ground. Occasionally it flaps its broad wings to maintain its speed. With precision and grace it continues to thread its way through the woods until its destination is reached, when it pulls upward at a steep angle and perches as high as its momentum will

Pellets of a saw-whet owl and a horned owl

comfortably allow. When flying, it is easily distinguished from other owls by its large size and heavy, direct flight; from hawks by its large head and very short neck.

The ordinary hunting technique of the great horned owl is to perch in a tree at the edge of a clearing or roadside and wait for prospective victims to pass beneath. The slightest movement or sound will bring it down in a swift, shallow dive, striking its intended prey with the full impact of its body and talons and binding its victim in a

An adult long-eared owl, smaller than the horned owl but strongly resembling it

A male horned owl, descending

A juvenile horned owl, gliding

viselike grip. So powerful is its clutch that practically nothing short of its own death will cause it to release its hold. Those of us who have handled these birds to any extent sometimes learn this from bitter experience. In one remarkable case a medical student, inexperienced with handling horned owls, attempted to pick up a captive horned owl from its perch. The surprised and frightened owl fell on its back and in defense thrust its talons deep into one of the student's hands. So fierce and unyielding was the owl's grip that it could only be loosened by cutting the owl's leg tendons.

35

The World of the Great Horned Owl

Horned owls also seek out roosting chickens, ruffed grouse, and other birds that may roost in groups in trees, often making regular visits to such places once the prey has been discovered. One case is recorded where an owl was observed attacking squirrels' nests at random, apparently in an effort to flush out or grab the occupants.

The voice of the great horned owl is an outstanding characteristic of the species, but is often confused with that of the barred owl, with which it shares the popular name, "hoot owl." Though similar in some respects, the common notes of these two birds differ markedly in pitch and cadence. Those of the barred owl are usually delivered in two groups of four or five syllables each. They are given with a rhythmic swing and strongly accented, loud, wild, and strenuous: *hoo-hoo-to-hooooo, hoo-hoo-hoo-to-whooooo*; this call is usually translated as "who cooks for you? who cooks for you all?" which gives a very good idea of the pattern and phrasing of the call.

The horned owl's hoot, on the other hand, is on a lower key, with a deeper bass and softer tone than that of the barred owl; but it does have great carrying power. When the owl is not excited, the call is prolonged, soft, and subdued, with little or no accent: *who-hoo-hooo*; or longer: *who-hooo, who-hoooo, whoo*. There is a sexual difference in the calls. The voice of the male is pitched on a lower key; his calls are more prolonged and elaborate, rich, deep, and mellow; the female's are usually shorter, simpler, and softer.

The hooting of a great horned owl in the distance sounds very much like the cooing of a dove, and we have frequently been led astray by well-meaning acquaintances who, knowing of our interest in the birds of prey, will report hearing owls near their homes but fail to mention that these calls were heard during the day, not night. Almost invariably mourning doves will prove to be the cause of such misinformation.

In addition to their characteristic notes, both the barred owl and the great horned owl have a varied assortment of other calls not so

36

A male horned owl calling, showing the characteristic posture

easily recognized. The barred owl in particular is well-known for its rich vocabulary of hideous laughs, doglike barks, caterwauling, and bloodcurdling screams. But the horned owl is also capable of similar sounds, ranging from weird, hollow-toned, and idiotic laughter to angry, growling notes and guttural barks. Since most of these nondescript calls are difficult to distinguish in the field, it is recommended that the observer simply wait for the bird to reveal its identity with a more familiar note—which usually happens if one is patient.

Horned owls respond quite readily to imitations of their own calls, even when the rendition is far from perfect. I vividly recall an experi-

An adult barred owl

ence on Cape Cod, Massachusetts, while in the company of Wallace Bailey, curator of the Wellfleet Audubon Sanctuary. We were standing at the edge of a small woodland pond one evening, at the far end of which was a fairly large tract of pitch pines. Wallace suspected that there were owls in the area and took the opportunity to demonstrate the effectiveness of a call he had been experimenting with. Raising his hands to his mouth, he proceeded to broadcast a call which is impossible to put into words but which sounded vaguely like a female horned owl with a bad case of indigestion. Almost instantly a horned owl answered from the opposite shore, and after some vocal exchanges with the bird,

The male horned owl that followed us around at College Corner

we were amazed to see it start across the pond in our direction, even hooting while in flight. It soon realized its mistake, however, made a quick circle over our heads, and returned to the other side.

Another time, while nest-hunting near College Corner, Ohio, we flushed a pair of owls from the vicinity of their nest, and both flew off some distance into the woods. I started to climb the nest tree, and my colleague Ron Austing decided to see if the birds would respond in daylight to his imitation of a horned owl's note. His call was quickly answered by the male, which flew in to investigate. It alighted in a tree

directly over our heads, though we made no attempt to conceal ourselves or to restrain our voices. From tree to tree the owl flew, hooting
vehemently as Ron called. Its hooting followed Ron's every movement
throughout the wood lot. It was obvious all the while that the bird was
interested only in the source of the sound; he paid absolutely no attention to me as I climbed the nest tree and banded the young.

Unfortunately, such responsiveness on the owl's part is often a
fatal mistake; many hunters take advantage of this weakness to settle
their own personal grudges against the bird, which they fancy is in
direct competition with them for small game. Some make quite a sport
of it, employing portable electronic devices which broadcast recordings
of owls hooting to draw them in. The hunters wear miner's hats with
spotlights controlled by gunstock buttons, enabling them to face in the
direction of the quarry with gun shouldered, switch on the light and
open fire, without fumbling around with old-fashioned hand lights.
Such practices are illegal in most states, but technicalities of this sort
mean little to those who willfully violate them.

Horned owls are generally quite difficult to approach on foot, seldom
exhibiting the tameness or fearlessness often observed in other owls.
Even when supposedly asleep on its daytime roost, the great horned owl
still retains a circumspective awareness of its surroundings and will
usually depart well in advance of the approach of a human intruder. It
tends to shun all contacts with mankind, and were it not for this fact,
coupled with its nocturnal habits, the species might well have been
extirpated long ago.

The owl, however, does have shortcomings that frequently lead to
its downfall. One of these is its predilection for dead snags or fence
posts as hunting perches. It is therefore a fairly simple matter to "pole-
trap" the bird by setting steel-jaw muskrat traps atop likely looking
stubs or posts within its range. Sooner or later, the owl is almost certain to blunder into one, a fact well-known to poultrymen and gamekeepers—some game farms trap as many as 50 or 75 horned owls in a

A steel trap on a post, an indiscriminate killer

An adult horned owl in a steel-jaw trap, hanging dead from the roost tree

single year, many of which are undoubtedly attracted by the large numbers of rodents which also gather at such places.

The bird's proneness to pole-traps, as well as its inability to learn by experience, is well illustrated by a case on record where a great horned owl was caught in a steel trap but managed to break away with the trap still attached to one foot. Two days later, the bird was caught by the other foot in a second trap set on the same post.

Naturalists have always abhorred the use of pole-traps even where the owl is not protected, since many other birds also favor such perches. The traps, of course, catch anything that happens to land on them; they are usually fatal to smaller birds and most often cause irreparable damage to the legs of larger ones. Though outlawed in most states, steel-jawed pole-traps are still in widespread use.

In Massachusetts, pole-traps are illegal, and furthermore the great horned owl is protected in that state by law. Yet pole-trapping activities have often been brought to our attention. On one occasion we found an owl hanging upside down from its regular roosting tree, a muskrat trap clamped firmly to its foot and the chain hopelessly wedged in a crotch of the tree. The bird had obviously run afoul of a pole-trap and had escaped temporarily, only to die in anguish at its roost a short time later.

Since most hawks and owls are quite susceptible to traps of this sort, attempts have been made to develop a pole-trap which will capture its victims alive and unharmed, for banding and release or for behavior studies in captivity. Perhaps the most satisfactory of these traps is the Verbail trap, so named after its inventor, the late Vernon Bailey, formerly Chief Field Naturalist of the United States Biological Survey, now called the United States Fish and Wildlife Service. This trap consists of a circular metal frame, about five inches in diameter, attached to a straight piece of steel which mounts near the top of a post or pole. A collapsible perch in the center acts as the triggering mechanism, and, when set off, the body of the trap flips a noose around the leg or legs of the bird; simultaneously two spring-wire "arms," to which the noose cord is tied, spring out in opposite directions, tightening the noose and

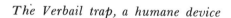
The Verbail trap, a humane device

holding the bird firmly. This section of the trap now jumps clear of the post and slides down to the ground by means of a long wire or cord. Here the bird sits unharmed until removed.

Verbail traps are especially successful in capturing birds of prey, and we often use them in our banding operations for the Fish and Wildlife Service. Though available commercially, they are expensive to manufacture (about six dollars apiece), so it is doubtful that they will

A horned owl in a Verbail trap

ever be adopted by poultrymen and gamekeepers, whose attitude toward any kind of predator can hardly be described as sympathetic. Moreover, unless kept under fairly constant surveillance, they are still potentially dangerous to operate: larger hawks and owls frequently inflict superficial wounds upon themselves in their struggles to escape, especially if left in the trap any length of time; casualties among smaller species of birds are almost certain to occur, even when the utmost care is exercised; and bobcats, foxes, weasels, dogs and other predators are an ever-present hazard to the helpless Verbail victims.

The great horned owl has a host of enemies, but few of them pose any serious threat to its well-being except man, who not only destroys the bird itself but is also responsible for great reductions in the natural habitat so essential to its survival. Where the owl could easily withstand the direct losses caused by mankind, it simply cannot compete with the onslaughts of the chain saw and bulldozer; and as civilization advances, its numbers will doubtless continue to decline, along with the rest of our diminishing wildlife. It is indeed unfortunate that man, in his eagerness to settle the country and develop its resources, could not have had more consideration for the wildlife he was displacing; for once it is gone from the land, it can seldom be restored.

Jays and other small birds fear all owls and never miss an opportunity to express their antipathy whenever one exposes itself during daylight hours, but by far the most relentless of the horned owl's adversaries is the crow. If there is one bird that the crow fears and despises, it's the great horned owl, and the long-standing feud between these two birds is almost legendary. The great horned owl is probably the only predator to dine on crow, to any extent, and apparently likes it as well as anything else, making raids on the nests and roosts of crows at night when they are completely defenseless. Whenever a crow discovers an owl by day, it promptly sounds an alarm call, the tone and quality of which has been reserved for just this special occasion. Instantly all crows within hearing respond to the call; a noisy mob quickly assem-

44

bles, cawing madly and flying at their foe in wild rage, but usually keeping a safe margin between themselves and the owl's deadly reach. Oddly enough, the owl seldom strikes back under these conditions, seeming to realize that such retaliation would only serve to infuriate its tormentors further. Instead it displays little more than dignified indifference to all this fuss and furor. When its tolerance of the noise and harassment ends, it flies away to seek seclusion elsewhere, with a long line of crows trailing behind. Often the owl is obliged to move several times before the crows give up the chase, but eventually they lose interest and drift away.

To say that the crow is an extremely wary bird and difficult to approach with a gun would be a gross understatement. But its compulsive owl-mobbing urge is one weakness which greatly increases its vulnerability, for when so engaged it has little regard for—or fear of—extraneous factors, even when they threaten its own safety. For this reason, crow and "varmint" hunters often use owl decoys—live tethered owls, mounted specimens, or facsimiles—to lure crows into shotgun range. The normal procedure is to place the decoy on a post, tree, or in some other prominent position along a crow flyway or in an area where crows are accustomed to congregate. After concealing himself in a blind, the shooter then waits for a passing crow to spot the decoy or uses a mechanical crow call to draw attention to it. Once the decoy is sighted by a crow, it takes only moments for every crow in the neighborhood to make an appearance, and the events which follow are guaranteed to leave the observer spellbound. Even as crow after crow falls in a hail of buckshot and a deafening roar, the remainder of the flock will continue their attacks, making this one of the more effective methods of crow extermination.

Frequently, red-tailed, red-shouldered, and even little sparrow hawks will join in the fun as a great horned owl is bedeviled by the bunch of noisy crows, swooping at the common enemy and adding their cries and actions to the general uproar. This is safe-enough sport

The World of the Great Horned Owl

as long as the owl in question is not a hunter's decoy; otherwise, they too will likely suffer the same fate as their black brethren, since most crow shooters are not averse to eliminating a hawk or two when the opportunity presents itself.

At times the horned owl's will to live is heroic. Recently Hamilton County Game Protector Dale Balser asked us to help him return a five-week-old horned owl to its nest, from which it had been taken illegally, under Ohio game laws. The nest was at the edge of a small, estate-sized pond in a residential area, and when I climbed up to replace the con-

Crow hunters with a horned owl decoy

fiscated owlet his nest-mate panicked, hopped clumsily off his perch, fluttered down toward the pond, and landed in the water, fifty feet or so from shore.

For some time the bewildered young owl floated there quietly, buoyant as a duck, looking from side to side. All at once he started to swim, using his wings like a paddle wheel on an old steamboat. He looked ridiculous, but the method was effective in propelling him across the surface of the water. Unfortunately, he had set his sights on a distant shore more than fifty yards away; before he had gone half that distance he began to tire, sinking lower and lower in the water as his feathers became saturated.

We had no choice but to swim out and retrieve the exhausted owlet from the icy waters, and finally I did just that. But when I got him to shore the little fellow was in poor shape: his body was limp and ice-cold, his eyes half shut. Periodically he would raise his head and gasp; I was sure every breath would be his last.

We wrapped the half-drowned youngster in my dry shirt and tried to administer artificial respiration. At this point we had just about crossed him off the list of the living, his condition seemed so hopeless. As we drove home, we turned the heater on full and rotated the bedraggled owlet under it as if he were being barbecued, in a last-ditch effort to dry out his feathers and restore his body temperature. At first he failed to respond, but half an hour later, as we approached our destination, he finally stopped gasping and opened his eyes to their full extent; at the same time his body began to shiver, the first signs of life it had shown since we fished him out of the pond.

Arriving home, we quickly transferred the owlet to the kitchen oven, turned the heat on a low setting, and with the door open let him bake for half an hour. Before long he began to hiss and snap his bill as we moved about the room, a sure indication that he had just about recovered from the ordeal. The following day we took him back to his nest, none the worse for his experience.

47

The World of the Great Horned Owl

We have intimated that the so-called "wise old owl" really isn't very *wise* at all and, in fact, probably has one of the lowest "I.Q.s" in the bird world. But what about the rest of the saying? Just how *old* is that "hoot owl" that seems to have been out in the backwoods as long as folks can remember? Chances are there has been a continuous succession of different birds, but there is at least one case on record of a great horned owl which apparently lived in captivity for 68 years—a ripe old age, considering the unnatural conditions to which it must have been subjected. Undoubtedly its wild relatives could easily match this longevity record, were it not for the ignorance of man and his efficient methods of extermination.

WINTER

THOUGH THE GREAT HORNED OWL is a perennial member of our outdoor society, it is difficult to picture the bird in anything but a cold-weather setting: a ground of white, frosty cold temperatures, and trees devoid of foliage. This is the time when most of our field work with the species is accomplished, and it is also the owl's busiest season of the year—for the great horned owl has the unorthodox habit of nesting in the dead of winter, often starting as early as February even in some of the more northerly portions of its range. Exactly why it does so is probably owing to the slow development of the young and their long dependency on parental care. Even with this head start on the nesting cycle, young great horned owls are seldom able to shift for themselves before the fall months arrive, with some begging an occasional meal from the adults as late as October.

In parts of this country on the same general latitude as Massachusetts, egg laying usually commences about the middle of February. As one progresses farther southward, the time of nesting gradually becomes earlier. In southwestern Ohio, for example, most great horned owls are incubating by the first week of February, often considerably sooner; in Florida and Southern California, nesting dates in December are not uncommon. Certain pairs within each general locality will habitually start nesting before or after the majority, but most will be under way within a given two-week period.

In accordance with the nesting dates, the related functions of courtship and mating are also carried on very early in the season. A month or so before the eggs are to be laid, the male and female horned owls begin their courtship. Although paired for life, they have a closer and much more affectionate association during the courtship period than at any other time of the year. Often they roost together in the same tree, feed together on large kills, and serenade each other with hooting love songs through the long winter nights.

The courtship display itself is a weird and ludicrous sight, with the male solemnly approaching his mate, bowing his head, ruffing his feathers, and performing other curious antics. Then, moving into position beside her, he suddenly pitches his head forward, droops his wings, and at the same time thrusts his short tail skyward; from this peculiar stance he swells his white bib in froglike fashion and gives a long-drawn-out *hoo-hoo-whoo-hoo-whoooo-whoooo*, after which he pops back to the upright position again. Now the female takes her turn, addressing the male in much the same manner and with a similar call, though noticeably higher in key and faster in rhythm; the two then continue to call and answer each other for varying lengths of time. Often throughout the ceremony they face one another and rub bills together, much as though kissing; usually the whole performance is emphatically punctuated by a staccato snapping of their bills, similar to the sound of a typewriter, injected at moments between the calling and caressing. These overtures to the nesting season are loud and elaborate, given with deeply expressive tones and gestures, as if the happy couple were announcing their intentions for all the world to hear.

Great horned owls do not construct a nest of their own but appropriate the old nest of a hawk, crow, or squirrel. When squirrels' nests are used, these are often scooped out or flattened to form the nesting cup; normally, however, the eggs are merely deposited on whatever debris may have accumulated. Though no formal attempt is made to reline or recondition the nest of their choice, it usually becomes more or less lined with fluffs of buff-colored down from the sitting bird once her incubation has begun.

50

A female horned owl brooding on a crow's old nest

Old nests of the red-tailed hawk seem to rank high in the owl's choice of prospective nesting sites, which is hardly surprising in view of the fact that the two birds have similar environmental requirements and often occupy the same woodland areas together. But even when their ranges are some distance from each other, we have known the owl to make drastic changes in nesting territory in order to use an old nest of the red-tailed hawk.

In one remarkable case the owls had been unsuccessful in their attempt to use a squirrel's old nest, and by the time they were ready to lay again, a pair of red-tailed hawks had a new nest prepared for occupancy nearly a mile from the owls' defunct nest, and on the opposite hillside from it.

A field companion, Philip Arrigo, had seen the hawks building this nest on a previous trip, and we returned some time later to ascertain whether or not they had started incubating. As I rapped the nest

51

A female horned owl incubating on a red-tailed hawk's old nest

Jack climbing to a horned owl nest (note red-tailed hawk nest in background, built after the owls chose this site; the hawks, however, were unsuccessful)

tree, a white pine, a shadow figure with ear tufts rose reluctantly from the nest, shook itself, and flew across to the next tree; to our surprise it was the horned owl from the unsuccessful nest, a bird we knew well by her distinctively pale coloration. A short search revealed the hawks' second but inferior nest of the season; it was in a white pine only a few hundred yards from what was now the owls' domicile and also contained eggs. Apparently their original nest had been usurped by the owls before their own incubation had begun, thereby forcing them to

put together another rather hastily, in time for the female to deposit her eggs. Just how near this female red-tail was to laying when the incident occurred I do not know, but from the looks of the second nest I would say that it had been a rather close call! Later in that season we returned to band one young horned owl and, coincidentally, one young red-tailed hawk, both very nearly the same age. The normal chronological order of nesting usually renders this impossible.

In New England and other parts of the East, old squirrel nests and other odd nests of questionable origin are commonly resorted to, especially when satisfactory hawk nests are not available. But where the great horned owl and the red-tailed hawk occur regularly together, the owl is inclined to be more or less dependent on the hawk for nesting sites. Often the two birds will alternate between two or more favorite nesting tracts, either in the same woods or in separate wood lots, as the owl follows the succession of old hawk nests, each year displacing the hawks and obliging them to build a new nest at the alternate location.

Arthur Cleveland Bent, in southeastern Massachusetts, considered the great horned owl and red-tailed hawk complementary species, one hunting by night and the other by day over the same region, but did not believe that the owls would tolerate the nesting of other raptorial birds anywhere near their own nest. In the Midwest, however, it is not uncommon to find both species occupying the same wood lot simultaneously. Generally they do at least tend to be on opposite sides of the grove, but sometimes they nest within 200 feet of each other. It seems likely that a more abundant food supply, which seems to exist in West and Midwest regions, reduces interspecific intolerance between the two, and thus the owl is not likely to dispute the nearby presence of the hawk. In other areas, such as New England, the owls seem to be much more aggressive in defending their ranges against the hawk, unless we are to assume that the meager red-tail populations of the East are strictly a matter of ecological instability.

In areas of virgin timber, or where dead hulks of a long-forgotten primeval forest still stand erect, horned owls are often partial to large hollows, broken-off snags, and decayed tops in old or dead trees as nesting sites. This is particularly true in the Midwest, where, despite the lack of extensively forested expanses, patches of mature beeches, oaks, and hickories are still fairly common, and isolated giants of sycamore, cottonwood, and maple can be found scattered throughout the secondary growth along stream beds and in wood lots. Such grand old trees, some five feet or more in diameter at the base, almost invariably contain a multitude of cavities, knotholes, and rotted depressions, thus providing homes for numerous birds and other animals, including several species of owls; their value as apartment houses for wildlife is immeasurable.

Old eagle and osprey nests also provide the owl with spacious quarters and seem to be popular in the limited parts of the country where these birds occur. Apparently the former occupants seldom dispute the owls' claim to what might well have been their own intended nursery for the season. If they return to find the owls already in possession—and once a female horned owl is settled in her new home, she is not easily persuaded to go elsewhere—even the eagle usually abdicates without incident, either moving to an alternate nest or building a new one.

Occasionally, though, the owl meets its match in stubborn determination. The late Charles Broley, the renowned "eagle man" of Ontario who banded more than a thousand Florida bald eagles, once found a horned owl and a bald eagle both incubating eggs together on the same nest in Florida. Unfortunately, a washed-out road prevented further observations at this nest, so one can only speculate on the eventual outcome of this unusual association.

We once flushed a juvenile horned owl from an osprey's old nest in the heart of a nesting colony of these hawks on Great Island near Old Lyme, Connecticut. It was about 20 feet from the ground in an isolated oak tree surrounded by salt marsh and some distance from the

55

nearest woods; another similar site was on a small island in the West-port River in Massachusetts.

Such open nesting locations are not commonly used by horned owls in the East, but horned owls of the West and Southwest often nest out in the open, and show an even wider range of nesting locations, depending on the environment in which they live. Old stick nests of various types, snags, and large hollows still seem most popular, but in their absence the owl will nest in caves, on cliff ledges, in hollow arms of the saguaro, a giant cactus, and in the deep crotches between those arms. They have also been recorded as nesting in barns and other build-ings, in the ruins of old Indian or cliff dwellings, and occasionally on the ground. Since horned owl populations of the West are generally much denser than elsewhere in the country, it seems likely that many of these unusual locations are the direct result of competition among the owls for a limited number of nesting sites. Under such conditions, no doubt some are forced to use whatever nesting places are available.

Snags, hollows, and other more permanent nesting sites are some-times occupied for several years in succession supposedly by the same pair of owls; but once a lesser stick or squirrel nest has been used by a family of horned owls for any length of time, it is usually rendered quite incapable of further service—unless the original occupants should happen to rebuild it for their own use in a following year, thereby making it suitable for the owls again.

Once the stimulating effects of courtship and nest selection begin to wear off, the owls gradually settle down to a much quieter existence, confining most of their activities to the nesting area and nearby hunting territories. They will seldom be heard through the nesting period which follows, except during food exchanges at the nest itself.

As laying time approaches, the female becomes strongly attached to the chosen nest site, roosting near it by day and even sitting on it from time to time, as if to assure herself that everything is in readiness.

The number of eggs she will lay seems to depend to some degree

Portrait of a brooding great horned owl

on the available food supply, or at least the number varies in different parts of the country. In the West as many as five eggs have been found in a horned owl's nest, and sets of four are not uncommon, while in the East single-egg clutches are often recorded. Normally, however, horned owls lay two or three dull-white eggs, which are rounded oval in shape, with a thick and rather coarsely granulated shell. Just one clutch is laid each season, but, should these be taken or destroyed before incubation is too far advanced, the owls will often lay a second set, either in the same nest or in one close by.

With the laying of the first horned owl egg, another nesting season is officially under way; for the next three months it will be possible to find nests containing eggs or young in various stages of development. For us this time of the year has always been one of endless activity and tedious work as we systematically check out countless wood lots and

57

make hundreds of hazardous climbs to study, photograph, and band our nocturnal friends.

In Massachusetts, the annual search for nests of the great horned owl is frequently begun on skis or snowshoes as the New England countryside lies buried under a thick blanket of midwinter snows. One year a hard-crusted snow cover enabled me to ride a bicycle across the fields and through the woods to the remote area in which a favorite and most reliable pair of horned owls usually nested. But normally, conditions are not quite so favorable—many a mile of horned owls' woods has to be tediously covered on snowshoes, often in wet, sticky snow which clogs the webbing of the shoes and makes each step a task in itself.

Enthusiastic as our efforts were, we seldom found more than half a dozen nests in a single season, from which one might conclude that the horned owl is not a common bird in the Andover, Massachusetts, region; yet we had nearly thirty pairs of owls under observation within a 15-mile radius of North Andover, and doubtless many more went undetected. The reason for this paradox is that most of these birds, especially those occupying poor or substandard habitats, are inclined to be very casual nesters. For example, a typical pair may nest for one or two years in succession and then be inactive for as long a period or longer before nesting again; others will nest every other year or so with some regularity; but only a few in what we might consider prime horned owl habitat will actually attempt nesting every season.

Such erratic nesting habits are difficult to explain, but are probably caused, partly at least, by a failure of the environment to meet the needs of the species. Apparently Arthur C. Bent noted similar conditions in 1935 in Taunton, in southeastern Massachusetts; he never found the great horned owl nesting in the same tract of woods for more than four years in succession. He theorized that the owls were such voracious eaters they exhausted the supply of small game in one or two seasons and were forced to move to new hunting grounds. Our observations seem to indicate that, rather than move, the owls simply do not nest when prey is very scarce.

In extensively wooded areas such as New England, locating horned owl nests is seldom easy, even when the researcher is thoroughly familiar with the owl and its habits. Our normal procedure is first to select a good stand of timber bordering on a fairly open area which provides suitable food and cover for mice, rabbits, and other small game. The next step is to determine the presence of the owls through such indications as prey remains, owl down or feathers, and, above all, roosting sites. An angry mob of crows, jays, or other small birds always merits investigation; then, too, we have often been aided by asking local residents if they ever hear "hoot owls" in the area, since anyone living near a horned owl range usually hears them at one time or another.

Habitat of mixed hardwoods and conifers (North Andover, Mass.)

A pair of saw-whet owls

Roosting saw-whet owl about to be caught

The roost of a saw-whet owl, showing "whitewash" and two pellets

When the presence of a pair of owls is suspected, the third phase of the search is begun—locating the male's roost. The male horned owl almost invariably roosts within sight of the nest, should there be one; but since he usually slips away well in advance of a human intruder, and the female is not likely to flush from the nest, chances of spotting either of the parent birds are not promising. Rather than try to sight the owls themselves, we generally concentrate on their telltale signs. This means ranging through as much woods as possible, checking

61

beneath coniferous trees for the fresh pellets and "whitewash" that reveal the whereabouts of the owls. Once the male's regular roost trees are determined, the female and the nest are usually close by, and generally not too difficult to locate.

In order to use this method of nest location successfully, one should have some idea of how to distinguish a horned owl roost from those of other hawks and owls. Fortunately, most of the lesser owls roost either in hollows or in habitats where horned owls are not likely to be found. Then, too, horned owl pellets are larger than those of most common owls but are somewhat less durable and often break apart before reaching the ground. They are very similar to those of the barred owl, so in doubtful situations, unless other field signs are present, we usually return quietly on a later date to verify the species by sight.

Pellet examination can also be helpful in determining the type of owl roost one has discovered. Horned owls are more inclined to prey upon larger animals than most other owls, and since the digestive system of an owl has little effect on bony material, the pellets usually contain sizable pieces of broken bones along with the other indigestible matter.

Hawk pellets, by contrast, show very little bone content, owing to a more complete or stronger digestion; loosely formed, like horned owl pellets, they too usually break up before reaching the ground. Hawks seldom return to the same roost for more than a few days in succession and frequently eject their pellets after leaving it in the morning; consequently, there is never any significant accumulation of pellets under the roosting site, such as one often finds at the roost of an owl. Hawks, moreover, tend to eject their excrement out and away from the roosting branch, whereas owl droppings generally fall straight to the ground.

While looking for owl nests, we occasionally find it necessary not only to identify each roost we discover but also to determine the time of its use. An early winter roost, for example, may or may not have any significant bearing on the whereabouts of the nest, and fresh signs are not always in evidence at the nest itself. Therefore it is desirable to know which roosts are in use within the nesting period. During the winter months, pellets and excrement decompose very slowly, but one can usually judge from their appearance approximately how long they have been withstanding the elements. The splashes of "whitewash," in particular, tend to break up rapidly in the rain and after a few rainstorms look like small chunks of chalk scattered under the roost tree. Pellets on a cover of snow, of course, indicate that the roost has been used at least since the date of the last snowfall. It is even possible to tell if broken pieces of excrement were originally dropped on the bare ground or landed first on a layer of snow and were then left on the ground as the snow melted away. When splashed on the ground, some "whitewash" stains will persist on leaves, sticks, and other debris long after most of the excrement itself has washed away; but no such stains are present when excrement is deposited on snow which subsequently melts from under it.

The great horned owl, like some other birds of prey, often has a regular feeding roost, to which it brings its prey to be torn up and devoured. This may be an old unoccupied nest, a wide flat branch of a tree, the hollowed top of a stump, or a hollow place on a fallen log. Such places are profusely decorated with the remains of the feasts— feathers, bones, fur, pellets, and droppings; they are usually not far from the nesting sites.

The movements of a breeding pair of horned owls are governed to some extent by available nesting sites within their range. Accordingly, any significant changes in roosting habits that can be traced to midwinter or later in the season are usually caused by the adjustments of a pair to their nesting territory. Nonbreeders or sporadic nesters, with which I had considerable experience in the Andover, Massachusetts, region, seldom move from the winter roost during their "off" years;

but any break in their regular roosting routine is always worthy of investigation, since it usually indicates that they have joined the ranks of the nesting population once again.

The case history of a pair of horned owls at Kenoza Lake in Haverhill, Massachusetts, graphically illustrates this point. For three consecutive years these owls roosted in a certain group of hemlock trees at the remote edge of an extensive pine and hemlock forest, near the lake, and to my knowledge never made a nesting attempt during that time. On the fourth year, as a matter of routine, I returned to check out the roost, only to find it vacant except for a few old pre-nesting-season signs scattered about the area. This seemed to suggest that the owls had either met with some disaster or had finally made a move characteristic of a nesting pair. I was inclined to believe the latter and began to search the surrounding woods. A fresh splash of "whitewash" under a new roosting tree soon caught my eye, and before long I was gazing through binoculars into the stern face of a female horned owl as she peered over the edge of her nest, about 40 feet up in a large white pine. In this example, a move of only a hundred yards or so from the old roosting area was sufficient to indicate the presence of a nest.

In the Midwest, a combination of smaller wood lots, denser owl populations, and less intra-range movement tends to facilitate nesting surveys and studies. Furthermore, non-nesting birds are far less prevalent, most of them being individuals that have lost mates or are too young to breed. In spite of all these advantages, locating horned owl nests is not quite so easy as one might expect, because of ubiquitous large snags and hollows that are all too suitable as nesting sites. Here we have discovered that a "whacking stick," used to pound on trees containing such cavities, should be a standard piece of equipment; when effective in dislodging an incubating bird, it saves us much laborious climbing. Some owls fly out when the nest tree is struck, but others simply sit tight until more drastic measures are taken.

One tight-sitting horned owl in a snag near Fernald, Ohio, had us

Descending to a rotten snag nest

puzzled and frustrated for several days. Numerous signs throughout the wood lot indicated the presence of a nest close by, but we were unable to find it by the usual methods. Once an adult was flushed from the immediate vicinity of a large hollow in a dead oak tree, which was quickly checked and found to be empty. Since the nesting season had been well under way at this time, we naturally assumed the nest to be elsewhere in the woods and continued the fruitless searching.

On succeeding trips back to this wood lot, the old oak tree was repeatedly rapped and checked carefully for evidence with field glasses, for it was becoming more and more apparent that this was the only suitable nesting site left in the whole grove. Finally I backed off into a nearby field with a telescope and, from this new perspective, could make out the tips of the adult's ear tufts at the lip of the hollow. Evidently she had gotten off to a late start this season and had not yet laid when the hollow was first examined.

We wondered just how much commotion the sitting bird would tolerate, for no amount of pounding seemed to disturb her in the least. The nest tree itself being dead and dangerous to climb, I decided to climb a small maple which branched out about 20 feet in front of the nesting cavity. I expected the owl to flush well before I reached the level of the nest, but instead she just sat there like a statue, staring me coldly in the eyes. After waving my arms and shouting a few times, I even tried breaking off some small sticks and tossing them at her from my vantage point. Still she refused to budge.

When it seemed apparent that nothing would be accomplished from that position, I descended from the maple and started up the nest tree itself. But it was not until the climbing irons bit into the wood just below the nest that the female finally deemed it necessary to move; once she did, however, she left the area altogether and remained out of sight all the time we were there.

Our records of the '64 and '65 nesting seasons indicate that snags and hollows are popular nesting sites in the Midwest. Of 86 horned owl nests found in southwestern Ohio and southeastern Indiana, 44, better than half, were in snags, hollows, and other such cavities, while most of the others were in old nests of the red-tailed hawk.

Also in the Midwest, it is advisable to take particular notice of any red-tailed hawks in the process of building a new nest early in the sea-

The female horned owl who flushed from the red-tailed hawk's old nest when Jack climbed to within twelve feet (most owls flush much earlier)

son; this often indicates that somewhere close by is the hawks' old nest, which very likely is being used by a family of horned owls.

The field techniques that we have developed and modified through the years have greatly increased our efficiency in nest location; but regardless of how thorough we believe our methods to be, there is still room for human error. Many times we have bypassed a fairly conspicuous nest site on our first trip through a wood lot, only to stumble onto it through persistent coverage later when signs indicated the probable existence of a nest in the area. It is truly amazing how easily the nest of a horned owl can be overlooked in the woods—and indeed it is fortunate, insofar as the owls' relationship with man is concerned.

SPRING

I

T IS OFTEN SAID that the first day of spring is not necessarily the first spring day, at least when the weather is considered. Across the northern portions of the United States the snow still lies deep, and some of winter's severest storms are yet to come as advancing warm air currents from the south meet and clash with cold air masses lingering in the north. Frequently these spring blizzards pass through New England with devastating effect, crippling transportation, disrupting power and communications, and virtually isolating some communities. Warm weather may not be far away, but for the moment at least winter still has the upper hand.

For some time before the opening day of spring, female great horned owls in these northern latitudes have been stolidly incubating their eggs through subfreezing temperatures, high winds, and violent storms. Often both the sitting bird and its nest are covered with ice and snow, but a devoted mother usually succeeds in keeping the central portions of the nest warm and dry.

The eggs themselves, moreover, seem quite able to withstand cold temperatures for incredible lengths of time, apparently without affecting embryo development. A field companion, John Campbell, and I once inadvertently flushed an incubating female from a well-concealed and inconspicuous nest in a stand of white pines during a fairly moderate snowstorm. Unfortunately, her premature departure and general behavior led us to believe that she was the male, and consequently we failed to notice a dilapidated old squirrel nest located in

69

Female horned owl brooding during a snowfall

what was then thought to be the male's roost tree. Instead, we continued our search through the rest of the woods for a nest with an incubating owl upon it. Some time later the endeavors of the female to return to the nest alerted us to our mistake, for we knew that the male would never attempt to come back while anyone was present in the nesting area. Back we went to the original tree from which the owl had flushed and saw the flimsy nest. After a hasty climb, I found that it contained two horned owl eggs that were rapidly being engulfed by wet, slushy snow. For nearly an hour they had been exposed to the elements, and I was convinced that by now their chances of ever hatching were just about nil, but I left them there anyway, in the hope that they might still hatch. Some weeks later, when we returned, this was in fact borne out; we found the owls raising a family in spite of our needless blunder earlier in the season.

Defense of the nest site by the great horned owl against human intruders is a study in itself, being subject to much individual variation. We are certain that at least two unstable pairs which came under our observation deserted their eggs simply because we had climbed to the nests to examine them. Some owls—even with young birds in the nest, which ordinarily keeps them close by—will fly off into the woods, perhaps hooting occasionally in the distance, but seldom showing themselves while human beings are present in the nesting area. Generally, however, the old birds are quite hostile and often quite belligerent toward an intruder, especially when their young are recently hatched. These aggressive parent owls fly back and forth above the climber, dive down at him, then alight in nearby trees, snapping their bills and hooting. Not infrequently they will even strike the intruder in their efforts to drive him away.

Such animosity by a pair of owls is not to be scoffed at or dismissed lightly, as anyone who has ever incurred the wrath of a truculent mother horned owl knows from experience. Veteran ornithologist Arthur C. Bent wrote of an aggressive pair that attacked him so vigorously while he was attempting to get up the nest tree that he was obliged to abandon the climb, "leaving the owls the masters of the situation." The stunning blows are usually dealt by a downward thrust of the owl's powerful legs and talons, which is greatly augmented by the combined air speed and weight of the bird itself. The sensation is rather like being hit with a club and slashed by several sharp knives all in one swoop.

In my own experience, I have been the victim of a horned owl blitzkrieg on numerous occasions, both while acting as a lure to draw the owls nearer for photographs, and also while banding the young at nest sites. In most of these contests I have had the advantage of such head protection as a helmet or fencing mask, but sometimes I have been caught unprepared by owls which I did not believe were aggressive. The first time this occurred, I was making a routine check of a nest I had discovered in a large white pine tree near Johnson's pond in Groveland, Massachusetts. I had only been banding horned owls for two seasons and as yet had not run into any serious trouble with defending adults. As I started up the tree, the broody old female flew off to the top of a neighboring pine. There she was quickly joined by her mate, and together they began to brew up a storm of owlish ferocity. I paid little attention to their demonstrations, being naïvely confident that none of these Massachusetts pairs was aggressively inclined. I continued without incident on up through the most heavily limbed part of the tree.

Upon reaching the nest, I started to sort out the numerous prey items which were strewn about the two newly hatched young, failing to notice that there were few protective branches at this particular spot and that I was well exposed on all sides. Apparently this was the clearance the female had been waiting for, and my bare nape was her target. I felt a sharp pain and vaguely recalled seeing the owl glide on past, after having delivered her "Sunday punch."

To this day I have no idea how I managed to struggle down the

A female horned owl striking climber a solid blow between the shoulders

tree. When I reached the ground and regained my senses, I found that the owl had opened three deep cuts across my scalp, from which the blood was freely running down the sides of my face. The wounds, though ugly and quite painful, were not serious. I considered myself fortunate not to have been knocked out of the nest tree altogether, and left the woods that day with a good deal more respect for the great horned owl's ability to defend its homesite.

73

The World of the Great Horned Owl

In our horned owl activities through the years, we have frequently found ourselves at odds with belligerent adult owls, and through these experiences we have learned more or less how to cope with such individuals. This knowledge may help the scientific owl investigator to avert similar—or worse—tragedy.

The first and by far the safest procedure is to go away and leave aggressive birds to themselves. However, such foolhardy individuals as owl banders and nature photographers seldom take this advice. Therefore, those who insist upon risking life and limb despite their better judgment must resort to protective methods which may help to increase their chances for survival.

The most important fact to bear in mind is that horned owls will seldom strike a person while he is facing in their direction. Of course, trying to keep track of two rapidly maneuvering owls while struggling up the nest tree is not an easy job. An assistant on the ground can be helpful by informing the climber of the whereabouts of the adult birds and warning him of impending attacks. These the climber can dodge *if* his reactions are quick enough.

By keeping branches, the trunk of the tree, or other obstacles between himself and the attacking owls, the climber can often prevent direct hits, especially in densely branched pine trees. These obstructions, however, also decrease his view of the maneuvers of the owls and make him more vulnerable to surprise attacks from unexpected directions.

An attack can be staved off by frantically waving one's arms at the onrushing bird. Unfortunately, the climber's arms and hands are usually occupied with other duties, such as clinging madly to the tree for dear life or wiping away the cold sweat which at such times drenches his entire body and runs down from his forehead.

Finally, the climber should talk to the owls with soothing tones to try to calm them. This sounds ridiculous and actually seldom accomplishes anything, but at times it does have a comforting effect on the climber himself, making him feel that he has the situation well under control.

Horned owls occasionally perform what ornithologists call the "broken wing act," in which a bird acts as though it is crippled and thus distracts the intruder from the nest. In her performance, the female flutters across the ground uttering short wailing notes, stopping here and there to beat first one wing on the ground and then the other, acting as though she were mortally wounded. Such behavior is much more characteristic of the long-eared owl, but nonetheless when a horned owl performs the act it is a welcome change from the reception that one too often gets.

Unprovoked nocturnal attacks by these owls on human beings at other seasons of the year have been reported several times. Most of these, however, appear to be cases where the owl mistook a fur collar or the person's hat or head for some kind of prey. Edward Howe Forbush, a famous New England ornithologist, once told of a horned owl that struck the claws of both feet into the back of a large collie dog. "This bird may have been misled by a white patch on the dog," wrote Forbush, "as the white on the back of a skunk is its favorite mark."

Incubation by the great horned owl lasts about 35 days. Both sexes are said to share in this duty, but in fact most of it is done by the female, the primary function of the male being to keep his mate supplied with food throughout the long incubation period. Should anything happen to him at this critical time, or until the young are at least half grown, the eggs or young may be doomed to failure, as the nest during this period requires the constant attention of the female.

The hatching of the owlets seems to have an inspirational effect on the hunting instinct of the male owl. In his apparent desire to provide well for his family, he frequently overloads the nest with enormous quantities of food, sometimes piling it so high with prey that

75

A male horned owl alighting with a mouse for the brooding female

Horned owl hatching

Horned owl just out of the egg

there is barely enough room for the young themselves, to say nothing of the brooding female. Almost philosophically, it seems, she settles down over the crowded food items in the nest in her efforts to keep the young warm. It is not uncommon to find the remains of several rabbits, rats, or comparably sized animals, with numerous smaller items, in a nest with recently hatched young. Arthur Cleveland Bent records one nest that contained a mouse, a young muskrat, two eels, four bullheads (fish), a woodcock, four ruffed grouse, one rabbit, and eleven rats. The food items from this nest weighed almost 18 pounds.

Since the needs of very young owls are exceedingly small, it would seem that the male's hyperenthusiasm is wasteful and unnecessary. But his added hunting zeal is usually short-lived, and the natural refrigeration at this time of the year preserves much of the surplus food in the nest until it is finally consumed by the adult female and her growing owlets.

The newly hatched young horned owl is an odd-looking creature, with an exaggerated oblong head and a short, stout bill. Its eyes remain closed for about nine days and, even after opening, seem to function poorly for the first couple of weeks; it peeps feebly and instinctively nibbles at one's finger, but cannot hold up its head for any length of

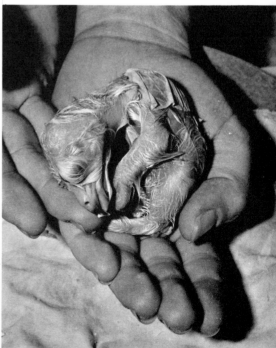

Four-day-old horned owl, showing the egg tooth

Nine-day-old horned owls

Nine days old, eyes just opening

time. It is covered with pure-white natal down, which is gradually replaced with a secondary, buff-colored down by the time the owlet is three weeks old. The owlet requires almost constant brooding by the adult female throughout these early stages of its development. It readily shivers from loss of body heat if left exposed to cold temperatures for even short periods of time.

78

The World of the Great Horned Owl

When the owlet finally opens its eyes, for nearly two weeks it sees little more than the underside of its mother's breast feathers. Even its meals are so arranged that it will not be exposed to uncomfortably cold temperatures while it is being fed. Unlike adult hawks, which usually stand beside or directly facing their young when tearing apart and distributing food to them, the female horned owl performs this duty from a more or less brooding position. She simply raises herself slightly over the young, draws the prey into the center of the nest, and carefully tears off small pieces which the owlets take by reaching out from under her breast feathers.

The young of nearly all hawks and owls are potential food items for other predators, especially when left unattended by the parent birds for any length of time. Horned owls frequently make night raids on the nests of hawks and crows, but these birds seldom have an opportunity to turn tables, because there are few times when young horned owls are left unguarded by the female. She is constantly on the lookout for danger and is well able to defend her brood against most other predators, whether they are nocturnal or diurnal.

Occasionally, however, the presence of human beings in the nesting area upsets the close attendance at the nest of the adults. If the female is frightened away from the nest, the unattended young are vulnerable to their natural enemies. One such incident is described by Laurence M. Huey in Arthur Cleveland Bent's *Life Histories of North American Birds of Prey*. A female Pacific horned owl was flushed from her nest by a human intruder. She was immediately set upon by a pair of red-bellied hawks which probably nested in the same area. While one hawk chased the adult horned owl, the other returned to the owl's nest, seized one of the young, and ate it in a nearby tree.

Even more remarkable is an account by Frank and John Craighead in their book, *Hawks, Owls, and Wildlife*.

After weighing a freshly hatched owlet and a pipping egg on a

80

cold day in mid-March [they wrote], one of the authors descended the nesting-tree and concealed himself several hundred yards away to await the female owl's return. Within 25 minutes she flew back to the nest with a dozen crows chasing her. Satisfied that the young owlets would not freeze to death, the observer arose to leave. The owl spotted the movement and immediately departed, with more than half the crows in pursuit.

The remaining crows did not detect him, so he continued to watch the nest. Four crows flew at once to the edge of the nest and then to a tree nearby. Nervous and wary, they jumped from limb to limb, looking at the nest and cawing loudly. One crow, bolder than the others, flew three times to the edge of the nest, only to leave immediately on landing. The other three cawed loudly, as though giving encouragement, but made no move to fly to the nest. It appeared that the crows had a definite project in mind and were summoning courage to carry it out. Finally the bold one flew to the nest, bent down and picked at one of the owlets, flew off, returned again, and quickly and deftly threw an owlet out of the nest with a flip of his bill. As the crow returned to repeat the performance, the observer interfered. The owlet dropped 40 feet, but was unharmed. There was a bruise on the tip of the wing where the crow had seized it. Afraid that the performance would be repeated if he replaced the owlet, the observer carried it to the laboratory and fed it egg yolk and sparrow liver before returning it to the nest late in the evening of the same day.

Several days later he returned and took measurements of both owlets, but on his departure the crows again gave chase to the adult owl. He suspected that the crows might repeat the earlier performance, so he returned to the nest the next morning and found both owlets dead at the base of the tree, each with a bruise on the wing tip as evidence of how it came to its fate. The crows made no attempt to eat the owlets.

When two weeks old, the young great horned owl is about one-third grown. At that time, as we have said, the first coat of white down is being replaced by a coat of buff-colored down, mottled on the back

A female horned owl feeding two-week-old young

with a dusky shade. Its eyes are open, and the irises are a pale yellow-ish hazel. It is still quite weak and helpless, spending most of its time asleep under its mother's breast.

At three weeks of age, the owlet is about half grown, clad in fluffy secondary down with its primary feathers bursting their sheaths. Its eyes are light yellow with pale blue pupils. When disturbed it assumes a defensive attitude, spreading its wings, snapping its bill, and threatening to attack. The owlet requires far less brooding now and is much more active about the nest, stretching occasionally and backing up to the edge of the nest to eject its excrement over the side.

At this stage of development it is not unusual to come upon a

Mother owl inspecting three-week-old young

young owl, dead or crippled, at the base of the nest tree. The reasons for such mishaps are usually difficult to determine—sometimes the nest has been upset by the wind, but at other times it seems intact. In some cases it is quite conceivable that the adult herself is responsible, either through clumsiness, when hastily leaving the nest, or in her efforts to brood the oversized youngsters. More often, though, the owlets probably crowd one another, in their first awkward moves around the nest, or simply lose their grip on the nest while backed up at its edge to defecate. In any event, such mortality has been observed several times in our experience. Twice young owls that were lone occu-

Jack banding a young horned owl

pants of the nest were found dead at the base of the nest tree; evidently crowding of the young is not the only factor involved.

Three weeks is also the ideal age at which to band young horned owls. Their feet are then large enough so that the correct size of bands will not slip off, but the owlets are yet too small to offer any significant opposition to being picked up and banded.

Banding nestling horned owls in Massachusetts is a relatively simple proposition. We seldom have more than six to eight active nests

A juvenile horned owl, four weeks old

to cover in a single season, and most of these are in fairly accessible locations—30 to 40 feet up in living pine trees. The only real risk involved is the chance of being struck by an aggressive adult.

Few Midwestern horned owls, in our experience, have ever objected too strenuously to their young being banded, but nevertheless our banding program here is a major undertaking. Not only is there a substantial increase in the number of nests we examine in a season, but the nesting sites are generally much more difficult to reach.

85

The World of the Great Horned Owl

Most of them are in mature or dead hardwoods, seldom less than 40 feet from the ground and often considerably higher. In the East, one needs little more than a short length of rope to visit a horned owl's nest; but in the Midwest, climbing irons, ladders, ropes in excess of 100 feet, and every tree-climbing trick one can imagine still do not assure success.

Often the snag nests are in dead stubs which are on the verge of collapsing under their own weight—and most certainly would do so if one attempted to climb them. Our usual solution for this type of problem is to descend upon the nest from an overhanging limb of a nearby tree, where this is possible.

One such nest, near Bath, Indiana, was about 40 feet from the ground in a rotten old beech snag. It contained two well-grown owlets. It was immediately judged inaccessible by my field companion, Pete Maslowski, and I fully concurred at first, much as I disliked the idea of leaving the youngsters unbanded. Then I noticed that, while there were no overhanging limbs close by, a branch from a neighboring beech tree had formed its uppermost fork some 30 feet above and about 25 feet to one side of the nest. It looked substantial enough to work with, and I began to ponder the prospects of lowering myself down to the level of the nest, then having Pete swing me across to it from the ground by pulling the end of the rope to which I would be tied. It was a daring plan, and Pete was skeptical, but he agreed to help in any way he could.

Slowly and painstakingly I made my way up the big beech tree. As I neared my first objective, the vital crotch, I happened to look into a knothole and was appalled to discover that its whole supporting limb, though alive and only four inches or so in diameter, was completely hollow inside, except for a thin layer of cambium and bark through which the life-giving sap was being conducted to the outer branches. Just how much strain this limb could stand, especially at such an acute angle, was uncertain.

86

Spring

I felt a twinge of fear and called down to Pete for moral support; then I put my rope through the crotch and tested it with a hefty yank. It seemed sound enough, but beech is brittle wood and would probably break suddenly and without warning. For some time I sat there, trying to convince myself that it was trustworthy but at the same time contemplating my fate if it should break.

Then I began to rationalize. Since the limb was obviously strong enough to withstand the storms of winter and sustain the foliage of summer, it should now in its naked condition be able to support my 200 pounds. With a lump in my throat I leaned back in my saddle and swung out into space, fully expecting that a sudden snap from above would be the last sound I would ever hear. Instead there was only the creaking of my rope as it rubbed against the smooth bark of the crotch. I breathed a deep sigh of relief; but still, this was not yet the supreme test—what would happen when Pete started pulling on the rope to swing me across the nest?

I lowered myself, until I was opposite the nest, and looked across at the frightened owlets yet some distance away. At least they were big enough to flutter safely to the ground if I could somehow manage to lay my hands on them. Fortunately their parents were nowhere to be seen.

Pete took the end of the rope and started pulling, gently, at first, but then more forcefully as I swung back and forth, closer and closer to the owlets. They began hissing and snapping their bills each time I reached the apex of my arc. Twice I kicked the snag with my shoe and finally succeeded in getting a toe hold in the punky wood on the third pass. I hung there momentarily but was unable to stand the strain. Again and again I managed to get similar holds, only to release them when it seemed that the whole tree was about to pull over into my lap.

By now my body was drenched in sweat and my strength was ebbing fast; I knew something would have to be done before I was too

87

spent to continue. Just then Pete gave an especially vigorous pull that brought me across to the snag. I grabbed for it and held on with every remaining ounce of strength in my body. The old tree lurched toward me, and from below came a deep groan from its rotten base. However, it stayed up long enough for me to toss the struggling owlets quickly down to the ground and swing triumphantly back to the live beech. Then over it went with a resounding crash.

It happened that my "swinging tree" contained an almost typical horned owl nesting cavity, at approximately the same height above the ground as the original nest and only a short distance away. It seemed like an ideal spot to leave the young owls. Pete wrapped them in a jacket one at a time and tied it to the end of the climbing line. I hoisted them up, banded them, and placed them in this "makeshift" nest, knowing that mother owl would continue to feed them there, and hoping she might take a hint and use the site for future nestings.

Young great horned owls normally remain in the nest for upwards of five to six weeks and are not really capable of sustained flight until nine or ten weeks of age. Nevertheless it is not uncommon for them to leave home prematurely when they are only a month or so old. Just how they manage to get safely to the ground at this tender age is a mystery, for though they are nearly full grown in body size, their flight feathers are not yet even half developed. Apparently they are rugged enough to stand the shock of impact when they hit the ground, probably using their short, stubby wings to help break the fall.

Other species of owls, too, seem inclined to leave the nest at an early age, usually quite some time before they can actually fly. We have often wondered why this is so; but in our experiences in photographing different hawk and owl nests, we have always been impressed by the failure of young owls to indulge in the vigorous wing-flapping exercises so frequently practiced by young hawks as they approach their fledging time. Could it be, in the evolutionary adaptation, owls of primeval forests being essentially hole nesters, that the cramped

88

Six weeks old and just off the nest, but flightless

conditions of such enclosed quarters prompted the early departure of the young, thereby allowing them the freedom of movement necessary to exercise properly, at this critical age when exercise is so important?

Regardless of the age at which young horned owls leave the nest, their first flight usually takes them to the ground. From there they readily scramble up a leaning tree or fallen log to gain sanctuary from

89

Juvenile horned owls just off the nest

ground predators and await further development. When approached they at first assume a characteristic hiding pose, sitting very still and erect, attenuating the body plumage and perhaps "hugging" the side of a tree or even each other if they happen to be sitting close together. Should this fail to work and the intruder continues to advance toward them, they are likely to panic and fly to the ground. There the owlet presents its most formidable defensive display, bristling its feathers, fanning its wings downward, hissing, and snapping its bill; at the same time the young owl crouches down, shifting its weight from one foot to the other, ready to spring at the intruder should he make an attempt to handle it.

One of the safest ways to deal with such an unruly youngster is to prod it with an article of clothing or a stick until it locks both talons into it; it is then possible to lift the youngster and seize it by its legs as it hangs upside down. Once the feet are under control the young owl is

90

Choosing an insecure perch, this inexperienced juvenile ends up in a vulnerable position, upside down

quite helpless, except for its bill, which is frequently brought into play and is capable of inflicting painful superficial wounds if one is not careful.

A fledgling horned owl less than ten weeks of age which has left the nest, and is capable of short flights, can still be captured by repeatedly flushing the bird from tree to tree until it tires and gradually works its way toward the ground. Before long it usually becomes flustered, misses its perch or tries to land on one which is too small to support its weight, and winds up hanging upside down, clinging from a thin branch or sapling. It is then a simple matter to shake the bewild-

91

ered owlet to the ground. By this time it is generally so exhausted that it does not even attempt to gain another perch but instead assumes a defensive attitude on the ground.

For the young of most tree-nesting hawks, nest departure is a gradual process. The young hawk starts with short hops to nearby limbs, before it is able to fly, and finishes with the use of the nest as a feeding platform long after it is fully grown and flying. But once a young horned owl ventures out into the world, its association with the nest site is usually brought to an abrupt halt. Even after it gains its powers of flight, it is unlikely that it will ever revisit its former home. Insofar as the owlet is concerned, the nest has served its purpose—as a launching pad into life.

Within the past five years I have had occasion to study and photograph the nesting habits of two different and widely separated pairs of great horned owls—a hot-tempered pair of "Yankees" from northeastern Massachusetts and a comparatively mild-mannered couple from the southwestern corner of Ohio. In both cases it was my good fortune to join forces with highly skilled and well-equipped nature photographers who were native to the areas in which the nests were located. In Massachusetts, my colleague was Torrey Jackson from Marblehead; in Ohio, my colleague was the co-author of this work, Ron Austing.

Photographing these two owl nests proved to be a study in contrast; even the nesting sites were markedly different from each other in the years they were photographed. The Massachusetts birds were using an old squirrel nest about 40 feet up in a white pine tree, while the Ohio nest was merely a decayed depression in the broken half of a large fork in a dead elm tree, about 35 feet from the ground.

Rather elaborate tree blinds were built at each site from which to conduct the photography. At the Massachusetts nest, two 20-foot 2-by-6s were nailed from a point directly below and on either side of the nest, bridging across to corresponding sides of a neighboring red

Jack inspecting the Ohio nest

maple. Then a 4-by-4 blind platform was nailed on this parallel super-structure just eight feet from the nest; finally came the blind itself, which was made of canvas supported by a light wooden frame.

The Ohio blind was very similar in construction but had a tri-angular superstructure involving three small trees. It was entirely independent of the nest tree and was located some 20 feet away from it.

The assembly of the blind at each nest was begun when the owlets were about a week old. This gave the adults a chance to adjust to the routine of caring for their young before we subjected them to the horrifying experience of having a small-scale housing development

93

The Ohio blind, completed

spring up next door. By allowing them to get used to feeding their young and become more deeply attached to them, we reduced the likelihood of their deserting due to our activities. We selected warm, sunny afternoons for the work, which was restricted to intervals of an hour or two so that the females might return to the nest from time to time and brood their young. This also helped to acclimate them to the blind as it gradually took shape.

The two females were utterly unlike in character. Aside from having aggressive tendencies, the Massachusetts bird was also a devoted parent. She left her nest only with great reluctance when disturbed, seldom going farther than a few hundred feet away. Even our noisy construction work failed to make her vacate the premises. She was always hovering nearby, uttering a vehement *"wac-wac, whoooo-hoo-hoo"* with monotonous regularity, closely watching our movements about the nest and threatening to attack whenever we ventured too close to it. If we ever had any fears of desertion at this nest, they were quickly dispelled by the adult's fiery attitude and by her instant return to the nest at our departure, often before we were out of sight.

By contrast, the Ohio bird was an extremely wary individual, seemingly much more concerned with her own welfare than that of her young. We were fortunate even to catch a glimpse of her as we approached the nest, and she always remained a safe distance away while we were in the vicinity. Except for an occasional hoot or squawk of protest off in the woods, it was difficult to be certain at times that she even existed. Though our blind was more than twice the distance from this nest as it was from the one in Massachusetts, the female's wariness made us unsure as to whether or not she would desert her nest while we were building it. We were greatly relieved when her acceptance of the blind finally seemed confirmed.

Our cameras—we used a Hasselblad 2¼-by-2¼ single-lens reflex and a 4-by-5 Speed Graphic in Massachusetts and two Hasselblads in Ohio—were secured on wooden mounts within the blinds, with numerous telephoto lenses protruding through the canvas and directed at the nest. Out in front of the blind, we clamped two strobe flash lamps to permanent stands. These were powered by wet-cell battery packs, in the blinds, and were synchronized to the shutters of both cameras. In order to see our subject in the dark, a flashlight was also tied in place, aimed in the general direction of the nest but not directly at it.

Photographing the home life of a family of great horned owls is never an easy task, owing to the season of the year at which it must be undertaken. The damp, cold weather is particularly unfavorable for both the photographer and his equipment. One must be prepared to face subfreezing temperatures, high winds, and rain or snow, together with all the common frustrations of bird photography. Enduring such adversities over extended periods of time usually results in severe cases of what we call "blind fatigue," a psychological condition induced by spending long hours in photographic blinds and continually fighting boredom as well as the elements, while trying to get pictures. To help prevent this malady and still maintain fairly constant surveillance, we normally worked in six-hour shifts, one of us taking the hours from dusk until midnight, the other from midnight until dawn.

Nevertheless, my first night in a horned owl blind was like some form of medieval torture. Shortly after sunset the temperature dropped to the mid-20s. As I sat rigidly on a hard wooden box within the blind, with scarcely enough room to move my chilled toes, I was sure that I would freeze to death before midnight. My back ached and my leg muscles were cramped. I kept shifting from one agonizing position to another in vain attempts to find a comfortable one, but nothing seemed to help. By the time Torrey came to relieve me, I was shivering uncontrollably, and for all practical purposes my hands and feet were no longer functional. To top things off, the owls had not fed their young; therefore I did not get a chance even to try my luck at photography.

96

Spring

Since we were anticipating rather lengthy sessions at this nest for at least a month, it was proposed that something be done to improve living conditions within the blind. After all, the quality and number of pictures depended largely on the alertness and keen reflexes of the photographer, and when his body and senses were numbed by cold and cramped quarters, he could not be expected to do his best work. Besides, we could never endure such torture for any length of time. Accordingly, a spacious extension was added to the blind which enabled the photographer to stretch out and relax in a warm sleeping bag while awaiting action at the nest. The installation of a small kerosene space heater at the Ohio blind also did much to increase our endurance, making photography possible during what normally would have been unbearable temperatures, even with the warmth of a sleeping bag.

Such "livable" conditions did create new problems, however: one was usually so comfortable that it was virtually impossible to keep from dozing during the long periods of inactivity at the nests. For me, a light sleeper, this proved to be a blessing, for the calls of the male birds as they announced their arrivals with food were quite enough to arouse me. I would then reach over, turn on the strobe, and be ready at the camera for whatever might happen. My colleagues were not so fortunate. Once they fell asleep, they usually missed the action altogether.

The initial reaction of owls to speed-light photography is almost universal: when the strobe light is first discharged, they fly off the nest in a panic, often collide with trees or bushes, and flop clumsily down to the ground before their eyes can readjust to the darkness. Generally the females learn quickly to pause a few seconds after the blinding flash before attempting to fly again; after doing this a couple of times, they usually realize that there is actually no reason to leave, and so they remain on the nest. From this point on, they pay little or no attention to the lights and shutters going off, and it is possible to con-

97

The female horned owl just after arriving at her nest

dition them to just about any kind of noise or light, short of jumping out of the blind and screaming at them.

One cold morning at daybreak I found it necessary to leave the Massachusetts blind, before my relief was to return and flush the female from the nest. Under normal circumstances, this is not recommended procedure. Should the adult owl sitting on the nest see someone emerging from the supposedly lifeless structure, she may become

98

unduly "blind-shy' or extremely nervous about the nest. This owl, however, showed practically no concern as I crawled out the rear of the blind. She refused to leave her nest even though I was only some 20 feet across from her in space when I started down the rope to reach the ground. She had obviously become so accustomed to our presence in the blind that it didn't bother her any more, even when we suddenly exposed ourselves in this manner.

We believe that male horned owls normally bring prey directly to their incubating or brooding mates on the nest, thus making it unnecessary for the females to leave the nest and expose the eggs or young. Both male birds that we photographed, however, were extremely camera-shy and conspicuously avoided coming to the nest itself, especially once they had experienced the sensation of momentary blindness when their pictures were first taken. Thereafter they would call to announce their presence with food and try to coax their mates away from the nests to relieve them of it. The Massachusetts male would fly from tree to tree around the nest, hooting once or twice from each location as he landed; in the meantime, the female would encourage him to come in with a constant, subdued hoot—a short monotone, guttural in quality —*oo-oo-oo-oo-oo-oo-oo*. This discourse would usually continue until the female finally lost patience, and left the nest to meet the male at some pre-arranged spot.

The Ohio pair behaved similarly, except that the female seldom even gave the male a chance to deliver the food, readily leaving the nest as soon as he called for a food exchange. Both adults conversed with each other almost entirely with harsh squeals of a kind usually used by yearling horned owls to denote hunger.

It is interesting that both pairs carried food items in their bills, rather than in the talons, as they flew about the nesting area and to the nest. Even such sizable chunks as half a rabbit or a muskrat were transported in this manner. Evidently the trait is characteristic of most owls.

Male great horned owl attending his mate

Feedings were extremely irregular at both nests, in accordance with the hunting success of the males. This in turn was affected by weather conditions, abundance of prey, and other variables. The size of the prey, too, meant infrequent or frequent trips by the hunting male. One large item, such as part of a rabbit, might be a sufficient ration for the young owls for a whole night, while smaller mice or passerine birds would be consumed as fast as they were brought to the

100

The female horned owl alighting with the leg of a cottontail

nest. Generally there was at least one feeding of the youngsters before midnight, and one or two about dawn. Sometimes there were none, but up to five feedings were noted in a single night.

Throughout the early stages of development, the Massachusetts male kept his family well supplied with food. Almost invariably there would be undevoured animal parts on the nest from the previous night as we entered the blind at dusk. These provided the young with an

101

early evening snack, which sometimes proved to be their only meal of the night when the male was not able to increase the yield because of weather conditions or poor hunting success.

The Ohio nest was always devoid of any surplus food. It was so clean that for a while we were certain that the young were not getting enough to eat. We reached this conclusion after alternately spending three half-night shifts in the blind, during which time we saw nothing brought to the nest; and we could see no trace of food remains on the following days. Though the young seemed to be in good health, we wondered just how long they could live like this, especially as their needs for food increased with their growth and age.

By midnight of the fourth night, we decided to take matters into our own hands. After cruising the roads for more than two hours we finally found a rabbit, freshly killed by traffic, which we quickly salvaged on behalf of the owls. In the dark hours after midnight I groped my way up the nest tree and left the hind quarters of the rabbit on the nest for mother owl to dole out at her leisure, certain that we were saving the owlets from starvation.

The following day, we were amazed to discover that most of the rabbit still remained on the nest. Small portions had been bitten off and consumed, but surely these were not the ravages of a starving family of owls! Though puzzled, we were determined to find out what was going on.

That evening we brought a kerosene heater to the blind to enable a full night's watch in six-hour shifts. Shortly after midnight the mystery of the "starving" owlets was quickly and simply resolved. Apparently the male owl was a very conservative hunter and, of all things, a mouse specialist. Each night he would harvest just enough mice to feed the family, generally making two or three trips to the nest between midnight and dawn. It was not until the young were nearly half-grown and the female began to hunt, too, that larger prey items began to appear on the nest with any regularity.

The mother arriving with a white-footed mouse

Another cause for anxiety at the Ohio nest was what seemed to be gross negligence of the young by the female, especially compared with the solicitude of the Massachusetts bird for her young. Often the Ohio bird would leave her nest, apparently of her own volition, and stay away for uncomfortably long periods of time, even while the young were still quite small. At first we feared that they would surely catch pneumonia and die; but since they did not seem to mind such exposure, we finally concluded that the mother owl probably knew more

103

The female feeding three-week-old young (note different pupils in adult and juvenile: cloudy pupils are typical of most young owls before they leave the nest)

about raising her family than we did. We tried to forget how wonderfully attentive the Massachusetts bird had been. Nevertheless, it was always a great relief to us each time that the Ohio bird returned from one of her mysterious absences and resumed her brooding duties at the nest.

The female with month-old young

At the beginning of our photography, both the Massachusetts nest and the Ohio nest contained the normal brood of two young. It was a striking coincidence, however, that each suffered the loss of one young-ster at approximately the same stage in growth—the critical three- to four-week age when owlets first begin to move about in the nest.

As we approached the Massachusetts blind early one evening, we could see from a distance that the female was not on the nest. We sensed that something was amiss, for she had never before deserted her

post without good reason. Frantically we lunged through the under-
brush toward the nest, fearing that some ignorant gunner had spotted
our blind and wiped out the entire owl family, which would not have
been difficult to do. Suddenly, the female flushed from the base of the
nest tree and started her usual protestations. This eased our anxiety
somewhat, but at the same time it raised the question of what she was
doing there instead of attending her duties at the nest.

The question was quickly answered. Huddled beneath the nest
tree was one of the owlets, which the adult was evidently trying to
brood. Though still alive, it had not survived the 40-foot drop completely unscathed, for it was obvious that it had sustained a broken leg
and possibly other injuries from the fall. Rather than return it to the
nest in this condition, we decided to keep the youngster under our
care and supervision, at least until the full extent of its injuries could
be determined.

The crippled owlet was immediately taken to a veterinary friend,
Dr. Edward C. Bulger, whose office was not far away. An X ray revealed
a compound fracture of the left femur. Unfortunately the break had
occurred so close to the owl's body that a splint of any kind would have
been useless. There was a sizable gap between the broken ends of the
bone, and the only way to set it properly was by open reduction—an
involved operation during which the leg would be cut open and the
ends of the bone bound together. Such surgery is difficult to perform
on a bird of any kind, and the owlet's chances of recovery would be
slim.

On the other hand, it was possible that nature would find a way to
mend the break and restore the use of the leg without surgery, especially in a bird whose soft bones were still young and growing. Dr. Bulger strongly urged that we simply wrap the leg in tape as best we could
and try to keep it immobile. If the leg bone failed to heal well enough

106

to be used, it could still be rebroken and set correctly by open reduction.

It seemed improbable to us that such passive treatment would be effective, but to be on the safe side we followed the doctor's advice. Within a week little "Peg-leg," as we called the young owl, was already hobbling around its box and seemed to improve with each passing day. Two weeks later another X ray was taken. It showed that a large bony callus had formed in the gap between the broken ends of the bone; the callus had fused the ends in such a way that, although the owlet appeared slightly bowlegged, it had almost completely regained the use of its injured leg.

And so it was that we suddenly found ourselves the foster parents of a bereaved and frightened young horned owl, a bird that was destined to join the long succession of orphans and cripples which have come to us over the years. In future months, "Peg-leg" was to become an interesting and affectionate pet; its curious antics and playful nature were a constant source of pleasure and amusement as it accompanied us in our photographic projects the rest of that season. Later on, when its powers of flight were fully developed, the youngster was allowed to roam freely through the woods around my home. It returned nightly to be fed, throughout the summer, but eventually returned to a life in the wild as autumn drew near.

Meanwhile our photography of the female and her remaining owlet had been resumed, but with some strenuous opposition from the adult. Apparently blaming us for the loss of her young one, she seemed more determined than ever to keep interlopers away from the nest and the surviving youngster. A night of photography now became a matter of who could climb to the sanctuary of the blind without being torn to shreds by an avenging mother owl!

We deemed this a golden opportunity to get some shots of an

Female horned owl striking Jack

adult great horned owl attacking an intruder at the nest. We flipped a coin to see which of us would have the "honor" of being photographed with the subject. With some reluctance, I, the loser (naturally), put on my leather jacket and fencing mask and once again endured an enraged owl's attacks for the sake of pictures!

Spring

At the Ohio nest, one night early in March, a terrific windstorm completely disrupted our photography and almost demolished our blind. We repaired the blind by late afternoon of the following day. At that time, both owlets were present on the nest. However, when we returned to resume photography that night, one of them was gone. It should have been an easy job to locate the bird, since it was less than half grown, but a lengthy search of the surrounding area by flashlight failed to locate the missing youngster.

At first we concluded that the owlet had fallen from the nest, had been injured, and had been caught and killed on the ground by a raccoon, fox, or one of the other numerous furred predators in the area. However, it did seem odd that there was no visible evidence such as blood spots, feathers, or down. Ron entered the blind as usual that night, but more with the intent of listening for the missing owlet, in case it was still alive.

Less than half an hour later, in addition to the raucous squeals of the young bird on the nest, it appeared that the cries of the fallen youngster could be heard about 200 feet away in the woods. At that distance, distorted by the wind and the incessant purr of the heater, the calls sounded very much like those of the female whenever the male came near with food.

Five hours later, the female had not made an appearance at the nest, even though the male had met her twice away from the nesting tree and had probably passed food to her. Ron felt certain that she had fed the other youngster both times, and he pinpointed the spot, but another diligent search produced nothing.

From that night on, the surviving owlet was all but abandoned, the female averaging less than one feeding per night at the nest. Once two whole nights elapsed without her return, and again our growing concern for the ravenous youngster prompted us to intervene and feed it ourselves.

Several days later, after repeated searches still failed to locate the

109

missing owlet, our speculations began yielding to reason. It seemed improbable that we could have overlooked the young owl for so long a time. Slowly we convinced ourselves that the owl must have been killed by a predator; that the squealing we heard was only the female calling impatiently for the male to return with food; that the female's lack of attention to the remaining owlet had been caused by the loss of the first owlet and also by the presence of our blind at the nest; that prey at the same time was becoming scarce and the adults were eating most of it themselves.

On March 19, the surviving owlet leaped from the nest at the age of nearly six weeks and fluttered clumsily to the ground. After sunrise we found it on the ground about 500 feet from the nest tree, with the female overhead, barking angrily. Leaving the young owl to her care, we turned and walked slowly back toward the blind to remove the camera equipment; our photography was at an end.

We paused for a moment, in retrospect, to dwell on the many trying moments we had experienced at this nest; it was impossible to rid ourselves of the guilt we felt for the loss of the one owlet.

The warmth of the rising sun was melting the frost on the leaves of the forest floor, and the air was sweet with the fragrance of spring. A flock of migrant red-winged blackbirds swept low over the treetops, calling as they winged their way north. Ron looked up to watch them pass, and his gaze happened to fall upon a hunched-up mass of down and feathers high up in a leaning ash tree. It was the missing owlet, exactly where we had looked for it so many times!

The early departure of the second owlet from the Ohio nest, before it could fly, was no doubt precipitated by its hunger and its instinct to join the family group; but other than that it was done entirely of its own accord, with no prompting from either adult bird. At the Massachusetts nest, however, the female assumed a dynamic role in her youngster's departure. This occurred one warm, balmy night

110

early in May, when the young owl was slightly more than five weeks old.

It was a lovely spring evening as I entered the blind for what was to be the final night of photography at the nest. I stretched out comfortably on the sleeping bag and was about half asleep when scratching noises from the nest caught my attention. I looked out just in time to see that the owlet had left the nest and was struggling up a dead limb which extended outward from the nest at a steep angle. Reaching the end of the dead limb, he squatted and began calling for food to the adult as she looked on from a short distance away.

It was difficult to calculate what would happen next—the owlet might return to the nest after a while or take the inevitable step which would carry him away from it forever. It seemed likely that the female would feed the youngster on the stub. In the hope of this, I proceeded to re-aim the speed lights and re-focus the camera on the stub and then settled back to await further developments.

Throughout the long night that followed, the hungry owlet called incessantly for food, but the female seemed to ignore him for the first time since we had begun our photography. Toward morning, a familiar hoot sounded from back in the swamp—it was the adult male with food. He was quickly joined by his mate, and for some time the two birds held a noisy conference off in the woods. During their discourse it was probable that a food exchange was taking place.

Suddenly all was quiet, but not for long. The female returned and alighted nearby and immediately commenced calling with her *wac-wac-hoo-hoo* note, somewhat muffled by a dead starling which hung limply from her stout bill. The owlet turned to face her, matching her calls with his own harsh shrieks of hunger, but the mother seemed in no hurry to feed him.

Presently the female took wing, flying from tree to tree around the nest. Finally she landed on the limb upon which the young bird

111

Juvenile horned owl just off the nest

was perched, about halfway between him and the nest. The owlet leaned toward her with mouth wide open, expecting to be fed, but the old bird held the tempting morsel just beyond his grasp and kept it there. This maneuver seemed to baffle the young owl. He stretched, strained, squealed, and snapped his bill, but he could neither reach the food nor persuade his mother to move closer with it.

After some minutes of withholding the food from the young owl, the adult turned and flew to a neighboring tree, taking the booty with her. There she continued to hoot and to flaunt the starling before the ravenous youngster, who had turned to face her and was all but falling from his perch in his efforts to reach her from where he stood.

Again and again the female repeated this unusual ritual. At last, the youngster could no longer stand his hunger and the proffered but withheld food. Crouching slightly on his perch, he spread his untried wings wide, then sprang toward his mother. Down he fluttered, far short of his intended goal, but in his failing flight, he managed to grasp a perch in a nearby tree and cling there instead of falling completely to

112

the ground. No sooner had he settled than the female was there beside him; she immediately passed the starling to him, hooted, and then cast a triumphant glance back at our blind. With the coaxing of the young owl from the nest, she had ended our photography of the family life at this nest.

Another of the few times we were present to witness the normal departure of a family of owlets occurred while we were photographing a nest of screech owls in a hollow tree during late April and early May of 1964. The brood numbered five, and the parent screech owls were catching and feeding the youngsters mostly June beetles, which were extremely abundant at the time.* Twenty or thirty feedings of the young were usually made by the adult owls during the first hour, sometimes more.

Flight shots of the adult screech owls bringing food to the nesting hollow were easily obtained, as well as a fine series of me being struck by both adults as I banded the young. One picture we needed desperately, however, was that of an adult actually feeding one of the young at the entrance to the nest. Ron sat in the blind night after night as the owlets approached fledging time, hoping for one to appear at the hole.

Finally the night arrived when a youngster did just that, but instead of remaining there to be fed, it paused only a moment, to cast a quick glance in all directions, then leaped out into space. Its flight was a short one, on a 45-degree angle toward the ground. As soon as it alighted, it rushed over to the nearest sapling and began to claw its way

* Editor's Note: Screech owls are very fond of June beetles, as evidenced by a captive owned by Alva G. Nye, Jr., a famous American falconer, while he was a student at the University of Pennsylvania in 1931. Nye often amused guests in his fraternity house by releasing June beetles in his room. Taking off in a buzzing flight, they were pursued eagerly about the room by the screech owl, which skillfully caught and ate them. Screech owls also eat, and feed their young, cutworms, grasshoppers, crickets, cicadas, katydids, moths, caterpillars, mice, shrews, moles, flying squirrels, bats, small birds, crayfish, snails, spiders, and many other animals.

113

A young screech owl leaving the nest

up the tree. By the time Ron had rearranged the camera and lights to record the action, the young owl was 15 feet up the small tree and still climbing!

Five minutes later, the second owlet also appeared at the exit hole of the nest hollow. It stayed there for less than 30 seconds, flew toward another tree, alighted, and then began to climb it. The third owlet, reluctant to try its undeveloped wings, merely climbed into the upper branches of the nest tree itself. The fourth and fifth owlets remained

Screech owl swallowing a house mouse

in the nesting hollow but, as with the young horned owls, were not fed by the adults for the rest of the night; they concentrated instead on feeding the young owls that had left the nesting hollow. Since these screech owls were extremely belligerent and not at all frightened by our photography, it is unlikely that our presence had any bearing on the apparent abandonment by the adults of the two youngsters in the nest. These two departed the following night. They were a day or two younger than the rest of the brood but were practically indistinguishable from them in size.

In large broods of owls, the biggest and strongest youngsters receive the most food. The food is offered to the young owls by the adults indiscriminately. The largest and strongest get the food first, and when their appetites are satisfied the smaller ones get a share. During periods of poor hunting, the whole brood might perish if food were equally rationed, which would give none of them the necessary amount. If prey is scarce, only the strongest nestlings survive. This is apparently another of nature's numerous checks and balances, wherein predators themselves are controlled by the abundance of their food supply.

Nest-leaving-time for the young horned owl coincides with the seasonal reproductive activities of many of the animals that are their staple foods. In southwestern Ohio, for example, most horned owls leave the nest during the first two weeks in April. At this latitude the first litters of fox squirrels, cottontails, and other small mammals are also newly weaned and emerging from their nests. Shrews and mice become more active, as well as chipmunks, flying squirrels, and others, some of which either spend most of their active time underground during the winter or hibernate. The great migration of birds is also under way, with its usual percentage of casualties dropping exhausted along the way, more than a few of which are destined to become part of the owl's bill of fare. The voracious, increasing demands of the young owls are therefore met, in a precise yet complex manner—as are those of all the other creatures that share the world around them.

116

SUMMER

SUMMERTIME, the season of abundance, is the time when many of nature's children first emerge from their dens or flutter from their nests. The first broods of most songbirds are just fledging, and egg-laying for second broods is under way.

By mid-June most young horned owls have been off the nest and wandering about for a couple of months. Most of them, however, are virtually no closer to becoming self-sufficient than they were at nest departure time. Gradually, however, the youngsters acquire the experience that will lead to independence. The creatures beneath them become less of a curiosity than they were, and one day the instinct to attack their prey is born.

Young horned owls are notoriously slow in learning to catch their own food, and their initial attempts at doing so are always clumsy. Contrary to popular belief, the young owls do not immediately accompany their parents on hunting forays. Throughout the summer they station themselves on conspicuous perches and utter almost incessantly their far-reaching food calls or hunger squeals until the adults return with food.

First hunting attempts by the young owls seem to be forced on them, often as the result of impatience over the return of their parents, or by chance, if an easy capture happens along. Youngsters that are generously provided for, in areas where prey is abundant, are probably dependent on their parents somewhat longer.

Even though the adult great horned owl is by nature one of the

A juvenile horned owl about five months old, showing feather progress

A young horned owl "putting on the brakes"

most savage and powerful of all birds of prey, the juveniles are often afraid, at first, of the larger animals that will one day be their natural food. Their first conquests, surprisingly, are usually over insects that even the smaller passerine birds subdue without difficulty.

Young horned owls that are raised in captivity and subsequently released in suitable back-yard surroundings invariably remain dependent on their human foster parents until well into autumn. Much can be learned from watching these captive youngsters, whose behavior and development patterns closely parallel those of wild horned owls. By supplementing random field observations of young horned owls in the wild with detailed observations of captive ones, a more complete explanation of their activities after nest departure is made possible. These studies help to avoid much speculation on numerous questions that might never be settled by observing wild owls in the darkness of their natural surroundings.

Of all the horned owls we have raised, Old Hoot has been the most interesting and the most sociable; he was the only one that failed to revert to the wild state after becoming a self-sufficient hunter. Old Hoot is still with Ron, although he is kept in a roomy cage for his own protection. In the spring of 1964 he was ten years old.

When first obtained as an orphan in 1954, Old Hoot was placed in an artificial nest in a tree in the back yard and permitted to come and go as he pleased after gaining his powers of flight. Like other owls raised similarly, he seldom wandered far and would return to the back porch each night to be fed. His day roost was usually in one of the large trees in the yard, although occasionally he would move over to an adjacent woodland.

Unlike the others, which gradually drifted away as their hunting ability developed (usually in October) and visited the back porch less and less regularly as time progressed, Old Hoot returned every night; we would see him whether he was hungry or not. One day, the following spring after Hoot was hatched, he disappeared and was gone for

119

several days. We were happy to think that he must have finally reverted to the wild.

Then came a phone call from a man who lived some ten miles away. He said a large owl, had alighted on his porch railing, peered in the window, and frightened his wife and children. He had rushed out with a baseball bat and clubbed the big bird to death. Only then did he notice the aluminum band on its leg. When he mentioned the episode to some neighbors, they told him they thought he had killed our pet owl. He asked if we would be good enough to explain what the band meant and suggested that the local museum might like to have the owl mounted as an exhibit. However, he added that the owl had been in the garbage can for a day!

We drove to the man's house to claim what remained of Old Hoot. But when the lid of the can in which he had been thrown was removed, we were astonished to find that Old Hoot was still alive! He was dazed from the blow, however, and it was three days before he regained his equilibrium and was able to stand erect. For his own protection we decided we had better confine Old Hoot, who had lost all fear of man. We built him a roomy cage and decided to keep him indefinitely.

Two years later we moved to a distant part of the county where wild horned owls are numerous. From his cage behind our house, Hoot would answer the calls of the wild owls at night, and often they would fly over and perch in the trees in our back yard to investigate this apparent intruder into their domain.

Some months later we decided to release Hoot after all, in the hope that he might finally drift away. We considered the fact that the resident owls, in defense of their territories, would probably drive Hoot away the moment he left our yard. Perhaps this would give him the sort of urging he needed to make him become a wild owl. When we released him, he circled the house twice and came back to perch in the old walnut tree. There he sat for above five minutes as if to get his bearings. Then he flew away across a field and disappeared in a woodland not far away.

About a month later, not having seen Hoot, we received a telephone call from Harvey Chrifield, a man who lived in a small town about three miles east of us. Hoot had apparently not learned his lesson about the dangers of landing on strange porch rails and peering into windows. Fortunately for him, he was greeted this time with a proffered piece of beefsteak instead of being bludgeoned with a bat. Rather than leave him with the kindly strangers, we brought him home and returned him to his cage.

One morning, almost a year later, we found Hoot's cage door open. That was the last we saw of him for five weeks. Then a telephone call came from Harvey Chrifield; Hoot was back with them, and for the second time we got him and returned him to his cage.

In 1959 Hoot crawled out an opening in the bottom of his cage and disappeared. Three weeks later he turned up once more at the Chrifields'. Again we brought him home, where he has resided in his cage without any further escapades. We have no idea why he flies away from our home area so rapidly, unless the wild owls are quick to drive him away when he enters their domain. In the small town, Hoot may have found safety from the wild horned owls. But the mystery of why he chose the Chrifields' house for refuge, in preference to all others in town, we probably shall never know.

Since 1946, we have raised five broods of orphaned horned owls, in addition to numerous single youngsters, and the young from two eggs which were artificially incubated and hatched. All of them were fed natural food, mostly roadside kills of animals they prey on in the wild. When the young owls were about five weeks old, we built a simulated owl's nest in a back-yard tree, where they remained until they were able to fly.

Of the many types of birds and mammals we have hand-reared in captivity, the horned owl is our favorite. Our experiences with them,

121

as they roam about the yard all summer, seem to be in marked contrast to those of others, who have depicted their captives as savage, sullen, and morose. Young owls obtained when they are more than four weeks old do, as a rule, tend to be less tractable, and when captured after six weeks of age they are savage and unresponsive and usually remain that way. Nearly all our young horned owls came to us before they were a month old, when they were much easier to work with.

The playful nature of our captive horned owls is by far their most outstanding trait. Almost a separate volume could be written on this aspect of their behavior. They are clumsy beyond belief and highly curious. It is endlessly amusing to watch each newly captured youngster go through about the same stages of trial and error, making the same mistakes over and over again, until at last the lesson is learned.

At the age of ten weeks, the young owl's wings and tail become fully developed. Each day at this age, the owlet gains more and more confidence in itself. Its short flights from tree to tree are gradually expanded, and soon it begins to explore small sections of the surrounding territory. The downy body plumage now starts to change, being slowly replaced throughout the summer by true feathers. By late August, it will be almost indistinguishable from the adult.

Aside from learning to hunt for itself, the first lesson a young horned owl must learn is how to choose a proper perch when alighting. At first it may try to perch on the tips of insecure limbs, or even just the leaves themselves. It is only after a few experiences with insecure perches, in which the youngster finds itself hanging upside down, that it begins to associate such inadequate perches with the inevitable overturn from its own weight.

Most other young owls also experience similar problems in selecting perches. Years ago, on one of my early hikes through an old beech woods near home, I came upon a young barred owl hanging upside down from the lofty branch of an old beech tree. Every few minutes it flapped desperately in an effort to right itself, but to no avail. Half an hour elapsed before it finally fell to the ground, completely exhausted.

Using their taloned feet as weapons of defense seems to be inborn among all birds of prey. When frightened, young hawks usually throw themselves back on their tails, presenting feet and talons to the enemy. Young owls fluff up their entire plumage and spread their wings to make themselves appear much larger than they are. All engage in vigorous bill-snapping and hissing. When cornered, it is not uncommon for them to actually charge the intruder, at the last minute jumping at him with extended claws.

The snapping of the beak, which is not peculiar to the owls, was for a long time thought to be produced by the bird's extending its tongue between both mandibles, then quickly withdrawing it under pressure. Careful observations with captive birds, however, reveal that the tongue is not employed at all; the bottom mandible is extended beyond the tip of the upper one; at this point, the mouth being partially open, pressure is exerted between the two, and at the same time the bottom one is quickly withdrawn to its normal position. This results in the closing of the mandibles instantly, with great force, much the same sound being produced as when a person snaps his fingers.

The use of the feet and talons for the purpose of seizing and killing prey, however, is not developed by young horned owls until some weeks after they are fully grown and on the wing—which is interesting, since their use as defensive weapons is fully developed even before the birds leave the nest. The instinct to pursue prey seems to develop rather quickly once they are on the wing, often far in advance of the instinct to kill. This results in the juveniles chasing and overtaking many animals with success, then not knowing exactly what to do with them.

The first hunting attempts of our hand-reared owlets usually involve the "capture" of June bugs attracted to our front porch after dusk. Harry, the male great horned owl we raised to help complete the photographs in this book, proved true to form in this respect. By mid May, shortly after gaining his full flying ability, he began to notice the movements of these beetles on the porch floor.

After some bobbing and weaving, he would glance occasionally in our direction, uttering his usual hunger squeals. Then, with a few snaps of his beak to punctuate his intent, Harry would single out a beetle on the floor and sail down to it from the porch railing. He would invariably land about two feet from the insect, run to it, and then lean over it with his mouth open—as if expecting it to jump right

Defense reaction of six- to eight-week-old horned owl, just off the nest

Harry on the back window sill, inspecting the canary

in! Nor was Harry unique among our owls in expecting a prospective meal to show this sort of co-operation; others have shown similar behavior when live mice were dropped on the floor or ground before them.

One juvenile great horned owl, a large female, once approached a white mouse with great enthusiasm; with one foot she seized the ani-

126

Harry at almost six months, roosting in the shade of our house

mal in a gingerly fashion, and it promptly bit one of her toes. With a shriek of surprise she leaped into the air, dropped the mouse, and flew away to the safety of the neighboring woods.

Another female which we kept for several years in captivity apparently developed a fear of all other living creatures. At two years of age she was terrified when we placed a live mouse before her, backing away from it as if it were a demon. She would eat only meat that was fed to her from our hands, regardless of what it was. It was only after she was virtually starved into submission that she finally came to recognize a live mouse as an item of food.

Probably due to their inexperience, young horned owls are often very active by day, as well as at night. While still in their downy plumage, they tend to be more or less ignored by their usual tormentors —crows, jays, and other small birds. But as the season wears on, they become increasingly bothered by their wild bird neighbors and learn to keep out of sight during the day. By late August the lesson is well learned.

Harry was on several occasions observed chasing pigeons around our barn at various times during the day, though generally his diurnal activities would cease by noon. Other tame owls have behaved similarly, but their daytime activities always decreased in hot weather or during the hottest part of the day.

Daytime hunting by wild horned owls has been noted by various observers, but it is never a common occurrence. It is probably engaged in mostly by young birds in low condition from insufficient food, while wandering about in quest of a permanent range.

Robert L. Packard, in the *Wilson Bulletin* (December, 1954, issue) reported that the great horned owl catches fox squirrels in daylight, regardless of cloud cover, by searching out and striking their leaf nests. His first observation was made at 10:30 A.M. on November 19, 1953, at the University of Kansas Natural History Reservation, when he noticed a horned owl slowly circling above the trees. Suddenly the owl glided swiftly downward at approximately a 45-degree angle toward a yellow oak. When about ten feet from the upper branches, it extended its talons and struck a squirrel's nest in the periphery of the tree. A fox squirrel emerged, climbed down the supporting limb to the trunk, and crouched there, facing the nest. The owl twice circled the tree and alighted on the branch which bore the leaf nest, facing the squirrel at a distance of approximately eight feet. With the owl's landing, the squirrel began clicking its incisor teeth and continued this noise for about two minutes until the owl flew away. Failure of the owl to attack the squirrel in the open is not clear, but had the animal not stood firm and remained facing its adversary, it almost certainly would have been captured by the owl. Possibly the owl was experienced in the art of avoiding the powerful jaws of adult fox squirrels.

In another area, several miles from the first location, on March 5, 1954, Mr. Packard observed a similar attack by a great horned owl upon a leaf nest, but no squirrel was aroused. In the immediate area of a roost from which an owl was flushed carrying a squirrel, several leaf nests were found mutilated externally, apparently by horned owls.

Mr. Packard's observations tend to strengthen what we have long suspected but could never prove: that owls may deliberately flush certain birds from their roosts at night and then capture them with relative ease as they flutter helplessly in the darkness.

During the spring and early summer months we commonly find plucked feathers of medium-sized birds, especially blackbirds, on the fairways and greens of local golf links. Until recently, these were always thought to be the work of early morning Cooper's hawks hunting the area. However, we now know that horned owls were at least partially, if not entirely, responsible. The clue was a single horned owl pellet collected beside one of the pluckings; it contained blackbird skulls which had been swallowed whole. Before adult owls bring avian prey to the nest or young, the head is almost always consumed.

The long dependency of young horned owls on the adults is readily apparent by their constant hunger squeals, which sometimes persist well into the fall. The owls that we raised in captivity and permitted to fly at liberty remained dependent equally as long. This would tend to indicate that wild juveniles eventually leave their parents' range of their own volition and are not driven away by the adults, as has often been suggested.

129

The spot on the golf course where a horned owl killed a robin

Although repeated mention has been made of our raising young horned owls in captivity, it is anything but the intent of the authors to encourage the interested outdoorsman to do the same. Even though horned owls make interesting pets, few people reside in areas which fulfill the requirements necessary for proper "owl-man" relationships —and there are *many* such requirements!

First and foremost, the would-be owl keeper had best live on a farm or other large estate, unless all his neighbors love owls! In urban or suburban neighborhoods, pet owls that are allowed this freedom are doomed to early disaster.

130

Juvenile horned owl drooping wings and oscillating with open beak to keep cool on a hot June night (note adult feathers on breast)

Our young owls, without exception, have gone through a prolonged learning period, gaining the necessary experience of their world. During this time, which often lasts for many weeks, they are extremely playful and may unintentionally inflict rather painful injuries on their human neighbors. This growing-up period consists mostly of mock attacks on various objects, from articles such as toys or wearing apparel (old shoes, for example) to dogs, cats, or even people. In an

131

urban area, even the owl lover must willingly sympathize with anxious residents when a bird with a five-foot wingspread suddenly swoops down in their midst!

Horned owls are essentially cold-weather birds, being well protected against the elements by a thick coat of down and fluffy feathers right down to their toes. They tolerate warm temperatures, but with visible discomfort. In summer, during the heat of the day, they often droop their wings, close their eyes, open their bills, and pump the muscles of the throat to facilitate breathing (an owl is structurally unable to expand its chest cavity in order to take a deeper breath than usual; instead, it hastens the flow of air by pumping its throat muscles). They are inactive and very quiet throughout the summer months, not perking up until the cool nights of late August and early September begin to foretell the fall and winter weather that lies ahead.

FALL

WITH THE FIRST cool crisp nights of early October, a gradual silence comes over northern fields and woodlands. The last chirps of katydids and other nocturnal members of midsummer's varied chorus are ebbing. Night-singing yellow-breasted chats have already flown to southern haunts, as have most other warblers. The mockingbirds have quieted, and the persistent, monotonous hunger squeals of another season's brood of horned owls no longer echo through the fall woods with the same vigor of dependence. Any time now, just as all others have done before them, the young owls will leave the parental range, never to return. Whatever it is that prompts the year's offspring to leave their parents is not known with certainty. The instinct to migrate, even though it appears weakly developed among horned owls that inhabit the temperate regions, is still present nevertheless. Even young horned owls of the southern latitudes participate in autumn and winter wanderings. Our recovery reports of youngsters we have banded show that they seldom move more than twenty miles from their place of hatching. After leaving the area where they were raised, they are apt to travel in any direction, quite often a northerly one.

The adult horned owls are strictly nonmigratory and maintain their home range the year around. Only in the far North, where the severity of the winter reduces the food supply, will the old birds abandon their range and travel any great distance.

Winter plays no favorites among wild animals, and all are likely to be faced with hard times before the arrival of spring. Cruel as it may seem, starvation is nature's chief control over such large predators as the horned owl that have no major natural enemies.* Adult horned owls, having survived past winters, remain quite secure in their home ranges, which they defend against all strangers as the season progresses.

In the north country, the periodical die-off of rabbits can have drastic effects on extensive horned owl populations, forcing a general movement or migration. Sometimes the die-off occurs earlier in the season, occasionally when young owls are still in the nest. When this happens, adult horned owls of one range may begin feeding upon young owls from adjacent territories or even upon their own young. Adults may even try to eat one another, with the larger females overcoming some of the smaller males.

A general movement of dusky horned owls in the Northwest was described in 1916. The ravenous migrants showed up at poultry farms of all kinds around Tacoma, Washington. The main abundance of owls centered on Vancouver Island, where pheasants, grouse, short-eared owls, and meadowlarks were heavily preyed upon. One of the more interesting features about this migration lies in the fact that at least 75 per cent of the owls shot (several hundred) were females. The main line of this flight seems to have been on the Pacific Coast side of the Cascade Mountains, and it was wondered whether the males migrated by another route, if at all. No record exists for a corresponding flight of males that year. Bowles, reporting in Bent's *Life Histories of North American Birds of Prey*, states that the females examined up to March 1 showed no indication of breeding and asks: "Can it be that the shortage of food and the consequent migration tend to slow up sexual impulse?"

Herbert L. Stoddard's study of songbirds killed by striking a TV tower in Florida includes a special section on predators, illustrating

---

* Editor's Note: Great horned owls are also occasionally decimated by diseases. In the *Wilson Bulletin*, Vol. 44 (1932), Paul L. Errington, who specialized in studies of great horned owls and other birds of prey, reported a pair of great horned owls from Wisconsin that had died of a virus disease which may be specific for certain owls.

that horned owls are opportunists, quick to capitalize on this kind of situation. Many other predators also competed with the scientific investigators for the crippled and dead birds, but horned owls were thought to be taking more specimens than all others together. It was concluded that, except during occasional "big kill" nights, few fallen birds would have remained on the ground for collection and study were it not for constant trapping and removal of the owls. As soon as removal of the owls was abandoned for a brief time, other owls would quickly move into the area to feed upon the killed or crippled songbirds.

Screech owls occasionally appeared to share in feeding on the dead birds but were usually killed and eaten by the horned owls as soon as they showed up. Several piles of screech owl feathers told the story, a fairly common one when the smaller owls venture out into open places where the great horned owl is hunting.

Stoddard reports that droppings and pellets showed where the owls occupied lookout perches around the TV tower as they waited for falling birds—or for some other unsuspecting prey to happen along. As others had noted, he found that it was the horned owl's custom at the TV tower to pull out the wing and tail feathers from small birds before swallowing them whole.

To illustrate the fact that owls are individualists, Stoddard goes on to say that "some may be much more destructive to our interests than are others. An occasional one goes berserk in the presence of large numbers of dead birds. One gorged so that it could swallow no more, but pulled the tail and wing feathers from an extra dozen or two dead birds anyway. These were ruined for all scientific use except as skeletons."

More than a dozen of the trapped horned owls were permanently marked and released at distances varying from 200 to 500 miles from the study area in an effort to learn whether the birds had any homing instinct. But none were retrapped and, as far as is known, none returned.

Adult screech owl, smallest of the "eared" owls and often preyed upon by the horned owl

The investigators at the TV tower believed that horned owls have only slightly better night vision than humans. Observations indicated that they do much hunting on bright moonlight nights. On dark nights they appear most active in the early dusk of the evening or as daybreak approaches. Most of the dead birds eaten by the owls were red-eyed vireos, but only those which were found lying on their backs, the white breast making them very conspicuous on all but the blackest of nights. Few of those lying on their breasts, with the greenish backs up, were eaten by the owls.

136

This was found to be true of white-breasted birds in general. One morning ten yellow-billed cuckoos were collected, every one with the dark back uppermost. The owls had eaten an equal number, probably those with the white breast uppermost. On very dark nights, the owls got most of their dead birds in the illuminated zone near the tower.

The conclusions of Stoddard and his fellow investigators at the TV tower regarding the interference of the owls, after several years' experience with them, is graphically summarized in the following paragraph:

As far as the horned owls are concerned, we are now reconciled to the fact that we will have to fight them every Spring and Fall migration for our share of the frequent kills. As we remove one owl, another soon appears and rather quickly learns when and where to look for dead birds. If the owl is one of a pair with a nest not far distant, dead birds will be carried to the brooding mate or young. We are compelled quickly to dispose of such a bird in one way or another. More than likely a mate will then take over the territory, "and learn the ropes" in ten days or two weeks, when we have the same thing to do over. Usually by late Spring, young owls are more or less "on their own," and begin to cut in on the limited bag at the start of the fall migration in July. They may get an undue share of the very limited but very interesting first Fall migrants until we have disposed of them one after another. This may be quite easy. Then come other wandering young birds [owls] looking for unoccupied "territories." If we are not "on our toes," they may cut in deeply on the large kills of September and October, as well as the small ones that follow. In November and December the mating and nesting activities get under way. It appears that mated pairs may frequently hunt the "tower territory" harmoniously together. Sometimes, judging from the scattered feathers, there may be desperate territory battles of owls not mated or related. In one case we found a great many feathers from two owls that fought savagely within an anchor pen; the enclosure was covered with their feathers.

137

A mockingbird attacking a horned owl

The World of the Great Horned Owl

The fall and winter ranges of adult horned owls in the temperate regions are almost identical to those inhabited at other seasons, since they are part of the over-all home range. Birds occupying fringe areas or second-class habitats may be forced to abandon their attempts to maintain a home range during severe winters or when prey species become difficult for them to catch for long periods.

Adult great horned owls from farther north tend to remain within their home ranges as long as possible and leave only when driven by great hunger. The juveniles leave earlier, beginning their wanderings in September and October. For them, fall and winter is a long, monotonous process of drifting southward in response to the mysterious wandering urge. Their ultimate goal is to fill habitat niches, or ranges, vacated by local residents. The farther south they drift, the more difficult it is for the young owls to find open territories, and the less chance the wandering individual has of surviving the winter.

Fall and winter mortality always seems rather brutal to us humans who pity the unfortunate animals that perish of starvation and the elements during this season. But in order for nature to maintain a balanced population among great horned owls, the mortality of juveniles must approximate the survival rate of the adults. Hence it would follow that if the adults suffered a 10-per-cent annual loss, the young must lose something like 90 per cent if a balance is to be maintained.

The fall and winter roosts of resident horned owls are usually similar to those of other seasons, according to where the birds happen to be hunting. When deciduous trees are bare of leaves, heavy growths of grapevine are favored for protective cover if spruces, hemlocks, pines, cedars, or other conifers are not present. The seclusion offered by needle-bearing evergreen trees makes them preferred by horned owls above all other trees when they are available. Probably they are not so much chosen because of their wind-breaking or element-shedding properties as because their density of needles and branches

140

offers better hiding places from such tormentors as crows and some of the hawks.

Although crows may actually strike a horned owl and even ruffle its feathers, the attack is usually taken in stride by the owl, who even appears indifferent to the proceedings. But hawks, such as the red-tailed hawk, sometimes strike powerful blows which may cause some damage. We know of one incident where an adult red-tailed hawk killed a horned owl by swooping upon it falcon style and dealing it a single blow. In this case, however, human interference had forced the owl off its roost into an open situation, and the owl was primarily concerned with the person, ignoring the presence of the hawk.

We have seen that horned owl roosts in summer are varied, since abundant foliage offers them such a variety of roosting places. Fall and winter roosts are more confined and also much more evident. Heaps of white excrement and clusters of broken pellets soon accumulate beneath these roosts, and, even though an owl may flush out well in advance of our approach, the telltale signs always betray its presence.

Pellets have been described as the indigestible remains of prey which are rolled into a compact mass in the stomach and later regurgitated, and it was noted that examination of these castings renders a fairly accurate picture of the owl's feeding habits. With a bit of patience, anyone with sufficient interest can soon learn how to identify the remains of the animals which make up the pellets. Working with a mammalogist simplifies and confirms identification of the mammals; with an ornithologist, for specific identification of birds; with an entomologist, for insects, and so on.

We have seen that pellet contents tend to reflect the relative abundance of those animals taken; however, the exposure of certain prey animals to predators determines to some extent just how heavy the predation on them will be. For example, white-footed mice and meadow mice may occur in equal numbers over a given area of mixed

141

Saw-whet owl catching a white-footed mouse

meadow and woodland. In short grass, the meadow mouse would be much more vulnerable to the owls and would be represented more often in the pellets because horned owls are more efficient in hunting the open areas. Woodland hunting owls such as saw-whet owls and barred owls would capture more white-footed mice.

Pellets accumulate beneath the roost at the rate of one per day and are regurgitated before the owl leaves the roost for the evening's

142

A collection of skulls of mice picked from the pellets of long-eared owls

hunt. Flying with a formed pellet in the stomach seems to be a disagreeable task for birds of prey. If an owl is flushed from a roost in late afternoon, it will usually pause at the first perch it takes, long enough to disgorge the pellet.

Grimm and Whitehouse studied pellet formation in a captive horned owl, utilizing X rays and radioactive material. Their summarization of the process of pellet formation is as follows:

> An owl retains its animal meal within the ventriculus by closure of the sphincter between the ventriculus and proventriculus; the pyloric opening, which is small and rised superiorly, probably remains open during most of the digestive process. In this actively contracting and relaxing pouch collect enzymatic secretions arising from the glands of the proventriculus, small intestine and pancreas. Although the general enzymatic action in digestion is little known, there is evidence that in young owls the gastric pH is distinctly acidic, becoming more neutral in older birds.
>
> As digestion proceeds, the nutrient effluent is pumped into the small intestine by ventricular contractions. Indigestible solids, e.g., bone, fur, teeth, nails and chitinous materials, collect in the inferior portion of the ventriculus, and are gradually forced into a tight pellet form. The length of time between feeding and regurgitation of a pellet is subject to both internal and external factors. . . . In the hungry great horned owl in our laboratory, pellet formation was essentially complete eight hours after feeding.
>
> Before regurgitation, an event Guerin (1928) held to be voluntary, the pellet lies in the superior portion of the ventriculus immediately below the sphincter. At expulsion, the sphincter is relaxed, and the ventricular contraction, with accessory contractions of the abdominal wall and proventriculus, force the pellet upward in a series of steps until it is finally discharged; the process in the great horned owl takes approximately four minutes.

Horned owls tend to shift their roost locations more frequently than most other owls and seldom show the constancy of returning to the same tree, or the same branch, day after day. Saw-whet owls and

A barred owl on an open roost

long-eared owls often return to exact spots on certain branches for weeks in succession. Different saw-whets are sometimes attracted to certain specific roosts for reasons unknown. At one of our favorite saw-whet areas, a plantation of several acres of Scotch and white pines, a single ten-foot Scotch pine once yielded seven different saw-whets over a three-year period. Each owl was found at the very same spot on the same branch.

Horned owls occasionally roost in shallow hollows, but this is the exception rather than the rule. And they never seem to go deep into cavities like barred owls and barn owls, although these latter two may choose roosting cavities of almost any depth, including shallow ones.

145

A female horned owl brooding during the day, alert to everything around her

The wary nature of the great horned owl seems to demand its constant attention on the world about it, whether it is on the nest or on the roost. It seems they never really sleep, but only doze. The slightest rustle in the leaves, or snap of a twig, will instantly bring them to attention.

OWLS AND MAN

Owls, throughout history, have been victims of ignorance and misunderstanding. Their nocturnal activities, serpentlike hissing, and eerie calls have helped to make them objects of superstition; uncordial relationships with other birds have also furthered the owl's bad reputation.

Although the ancient Greeks seemed to respect Pallas Athene and displayed the owl goddess on coins of the period, the Romans believed that the birds were messengers of death. Everyone trembled with fear if an owl flew above a town or alighted on a housetop. One blundered into the capital, was captured, burned, and its ashes thrown into the Tiber River. The deaths of several Roman emperors were said to be presaged when owls landed on their homes.

Classical literature abounds in derogatory references to owls, and writers and composers have often taken advantage of their black repute to enhance scenes of horror. "The obscure bird [owl] clamored the live-long night" before the murder of Duncan in Shakespeare's *Macbeth*. And in the ballet of Tchaikovsky's *Swan Lake*, Rothbart, the evil magician, disguises himself as an owl in order to spy on the swan maidens.

Owls were also thought to be in league with witches, carrying them through the night on noiseless wings or contributing materials to their magic brews. "The owlet's wing," writes J. B. Harting, "was an ingredient in the cauldron wherein the witches prepared their 'charm of powerful trouble'" (*Macbeth*, iv, I). Nor was their association with

147

disciples of evil limited to witches alone: the people of Tangier considered common barn owls "the clairvoyant friends of the Devil."

Even today in central India the owl is generally regarded as a bird of ill omen. "If one happens to perch on the house of a native, it is a sign that one of his household will die, or some other misfortune will befall him within a year. This can only be averted by giving the house or its value in money to the Brahmins, or making extraordinary peace-offerings to the gods." In Sweden the owl is thought to be a tool of sorcery, and people there use great caution in speaking of them for fear of being ensnared.

While most of these popular misconceptions have roots deep in Eurasian fable and folklore, some New World cultures, too, were more or less influenced by owls. Most American Indians seem to have regarded the birds without much superstition; but the ancient Mexicans and Mayas of Yucatan used them in ceremonial rituals, and some remarkable designs involving the great horned owl are found in their wood and stone carvings.

Despite widespread acceptance in Europe and Asia of the supernatural affiliations of owls, the myth did not often carry over into this country. But Pennsylvania Dutch ancestors, a highly superstitious folk, perpetuated some of the Old World beliefs, and even now many of their descendants will not allow anyone to tamper with owls that are nesting or roosting on their property. And the superstitious Negroes of the south will warn one to turn back from any journey if a screech owl cries above. An old hoot owl, however, may fortell either good or bad fortune, depending on whether its hoots come from the right or left hand. This sign is unfailing, and especially heeded in 'coon or 'possum hunting at night; three hoots from the left will send any hunter home in defeat.

For the most part, though, the settlers of this country were hard-nosed realists and dealt in the cold facts of survival. They had little use for owls or other birds of prey, since these "varmints" stole chickens and depleted the supply of natural game and songbirds valued by man. Predation was considered competition and was dealt with by campaigns of extermination under the bounty system.

Many pioneer naturalists recognized the need for legislation to protect birds of prey but knew that this radical proposal would probably meet with stiff opposition. They needed scientific evidence to substantiate claims that most of these birds were worth protecting. Accordingly, food-habit studies were conducted and the results, brought to public attention, dispelled many common beliefs of the day. On the basis of these findings, hawks and owls were judged by the economic importance of what they ate. Those feeding mostly on rodents and insects were labeled "good" or beneficial; those which fed to any extent on game, poultry, or songbirds were usually condemned as harmful or "bad." Species such as the Cooper's hawk and the great horned owl were often scapegoats, portrayed as ferocious villains and responsible for giving the rest of the clan a bad name; it was undoubtedly true that an individual bird might be a nuisance around farmyards where chickens and ducks were allowed to rove at will.

The work of these early conservationists was helpful in turning public sentiment in favor of birds of prey as a group. But remaining prejudice against such species as the great horned owl has been difficult to overcome.

At first, laws in many states protected only those birds that were considered beneficial and excluded the so-called "destructive" predators. Such legislation, however, soon proved ineffectual and virtually impossible to enforce: a violator needed only to plead that he thought he was destroying an unprotected species, and usually the case would be dropped. It was easy to see that more stringent and precise laws were necessary. In recognition of this, most enlightened states now have "model" hawk and owl laws to protect all birds of prey, except

149

when they are caught in the act of doing actual damage to personal property.

But bird-protection laws are meaningless unless they are enforced and supplemented by programs to teach us the value of each bird in its natural environment. It has only been during fairly recent times that we have come more fully to understand and appreciate that predation is vital to maintaining balance of our wildlife structure. We have made great strides in conservation since the days when predators were viewed only in an economic light. But as long as the horned owl remains on the unprotected list, as it does in many states, we still have a long way to go toward preserving our birds of prey.

GREAT HORNED OWL SUBSPECIES

GREAT HORNED OWLS inhabit a wide range throughout North America and are separated by ornithologists into ten geographical races or subspecies. According to the Check List of the American Ornithologists' Union (1957 edition), these are as follows:

1. The Great Horned Owl, *Bubo virginianus virginianus*, nests from southern Ontario, southern Quebec, western New Brunswick, and Nova Scotia south to the Gulf coast and throughout Florida and west to Wisconsin, eastern Minnesota, southeastern South Dakota, eastern Kansas, eastern Oklahoma, and eastern Texas. This race might be considered an intermediate form in the extremes of color variation shown by the species, being neither very light nor very dark. In the adults, the sexes are alike but variable in size and color. The upper parts are mottled, speckled, and vermiculated with brownish-black on a dull grayish-brown or ochraceous ground; the darker color usually predominates on top of the head and on the back. Flight feathers are barred with dark and light colors, and the tail is crossed by about seven blackish or dusky bands. Both the wings and the tail show dusky mottling on the lighter bars. The throat is white; this often extends down to the center of the breast. The rest of the plumage is ochraceous, buff, or tawny, mostly barred narrowly, blackish across, and dappled or striped black lengthwise on the upper breast; legs and feet are usually marked, but sometimes unmarked. The face is chiefly tawny or rusty, bordered by black; the bill and claws are black; the eyes have irises of bright yellow to pale yellow or straw.

151

The World of the Great Horned Owl

2. The Western Horned Owl, *Bubo virginianus pallescens*, nests from southeastern California, southern Nevada, southern Utah, northern New Mexico, and north-central Texas south to the Mojave Desert, Lower California, and into northern Mexico. This is a paler subspecies than the eastern Great Horned Owl but is essentially similar in other respects.

3. The Arctic Horned Owl, *Bubo virginianus wapacuthu,* nests from the tree limit in the Mackenzie Valley to Hudson Bay and in northeastern British Columbia to central Alberta, Saskatchewan, Manitoba, and northern Ontario. It is much paler than the so-called typical Great Horned Owl; some are as white as snowy owls.

4. The Dusky Horned Owl, *Bubo virginianus saturatus,* is a bird of the humid forests of the Pacific coast region from northern California, Oregon, and Washington north through British Columbia to Alaska. It is the darkest of the horned owls but is similar in habits to other western subspecies.

5. The Labrador Horned Owl, *Bubo virginianus heterocnemis,* ranges from the northern portions of Labrador and Newfoundland south through New England to Connecticut. It is a large and dark bird with larger bill and paler lower parts than the Dusky Horned Owl.

6. The Pacific Horned Owl, *Bubo virginianus pacificus,* is essentially the horned owl of California. It lives in wooded river bottoms, foothill ravines, and mountain forests up to 7,000 feet (except along the humid northwest coastal strip) south to Lower California and east to west-central Nevada. It is slightly smaller and darker than the Western Horned Owl.

7. The Montana Horned Owl, *Bubo virginianus occidentalis,* occurs from southeastern Oregon, central Alberta, Montana, southern Saskatchewan, southern Manitoba, South Dakota, and Minnesota south to eastern and southern Idaho, central Nevada, central Utah, Colorado, Kansas, and northeastern California.

8. The St. Michael Horned Owl, *Bubo virginianus algistus,* occupies the coastal regions of Alaska from Bristol Bay and the Yukon delta northward. It is larger than the Pacific Horned Owl and may be separated from the Montana Horned Owl by its darker upper surfaces and somewhat less heavily barred lower surfaces.

9. The Northwestern Horned Owl, *Bubo virginianus lagophonus,* ranges from Cook Inlet and the interior of Alaska and the Yukon south through central and eastern British Columbia, eastern Washington, northeastern Oregon, and northern Idaho to northwestern Montana. This subspecies is nearer in color to the Dusky Horned Owl than to any other form, but it is not quite so dark.

10. The Dwarf Horned Owl, *Bubo virginianus elachistus,* inhabits the southern part of Lower California and never occurs in the United States. It has two very distinct color phases, one light, the other dark; both are substantially smaller than other horned owls.

Although horned owls show considerable variation in plumage coloration, there seem to be no authentic records of albinism, erythrism, or melanism within the species.

BIBLIOGRAPHY

Allen, Durward L. *Our Wildlife Legacy*, rev. ed. New York: Funk & Wagnalls Company, 1962.

Allen, Glover M. *Birds and Their Attributes*. Gloucester, Mass.: Peter Smith, 1925.

Austin, Oliver L., Jr. "An Interesting Horned Owl Capture," *Bird-Banding* (Vol. 3, 1932, p. 33).

Bent, Arthur C. *Life Histories of North American Birds of Prey* (Part 2, Bulletin 170). Washington, D.C.: U.S. National Museum, 1937.

Brockway, Arthur W. "Large Flight of Great Horned Owls and Goshawks at Hadlyme, Connecticut," *Auk* (Vol. 35, 1918, pp. 351–352).

Cook, George L. "Notes on the Western Horned Owl," *Oologist*, (Vol. 43, 1926, p. 18).

Craighead, Frank C., Jr., and John J. *Hawks, Owls, and Wildlife*. Harrisburg, Pa.: The Stackpole Co., and Washington, D.C.: Wildlife Management Institute, 1956.

Donahue, Ralph J. "The Nesting of a Great Horned Owl," *Oologist* (Vol. 40, 1923, pp. 135–136).

Errington, Paul L., and Hamerstrom, F. N. and Frances *The Great Horned Owl and Its Prey in North-Central United States*. Research Bulletin 277, Ames, Iowa: Iowa State College, 1940.

Errington, Paul L. "Studies on the Behavior of the Great Horned Owl," *Wilson Bulletin* (Vol. 44, Dec., 1932, pp. 212–220).

Forbush, Edward H. *Birds of Massachusetts and Other New England States* (Vol. 2) Norwood, Mass.: Massachusetts Department of Agriculture, 1929.

Grimm, Robert J., and Whitehouse, Walter M. "Pellet Formation in a Great Horned Owl: A Roentgenographic Study," *Auk* (Vol. 80, July, 1963, pp. 301–306).

Hagar, Donald C. "Nesting Populations of Red-tailed Hawks and Great Horned Owls in Central New York State," *Wilson Bulletin* (Vol. 69, Sept., 1957, p. 263).

Hallman, Roy C. "A Nest of Great Horned Owls," *Florida Naturalist* (Vol. 2, 1929, pp. 99–100).

Huey, Laurence M. "Skunks as Prey for Owls," *Wilson Bulletin* (Vol. 43, 1931, p. 224).

Ingersoll, Ernest. *Birds in Legend, Fable, and Folklore.*

Jackson, Ralph W. "Strange Behavior of Great Horned Owl in Behalf of Young," *Auk* (Vol. 42, 1925, p. 445).

Kelso, Leon. "Some Night Observations on the Western Horned Owl," *Condor* (Vol. 32, 1929, pp. 126–127).

Keyes, Charles R. "A History of Certain Great Horned Owls," *Condor* (Vol. 13, 1911, pp. 5–9).

Little, Robert. "Great Horned Owl," *Cardinal* (Vol. 3, 1931, pp. 17–18).

Nicholson, Donald J. "Horned Owl Shrewdness and Ferocity," *Oologist* (Vol. 43, 1926, p. 14).

Norton, Arthur H. "Watching a Pair of Great Horned Owls," *Maine Field Naturalist* (Vol. 8, 1928, pp. 3–16).

Oberholser, Harry C. "A Revision of American Great Horned Owls," *Proceedings of the U.S. National Museum* (Vol. 27, 1904, pp. 177–192).

Peterson, Roger T., and the Editors of Life. *The Birds* (Life Nature Library). New York: Time, Inc., 1963.

Peterson, Roger T. "Eagle Man," *Audubon Magazine* (January–February 1948 issue).

Pettingill, Olin S., Jr. *A Laboratory and Field Manual of Ornithology.* Minneapolis, Minn.: Burgess Publishing Co., 1958.

Reed, Bessie P. "Growth Developments and Reactions of Young Great Horned Owls," *Auk* (Vol. 42, 1925, pp. 14–31).

Richardson, Charles H., Jr. "Cannibalism in Owls," *Condor* (Vol. 8, 1906, p. 57).

Soper, Joseph D. "Flight of Horned Owls in Canada," *Auk* (Vol. 35, 1918, pp. 478–479).

Stoner, Emerson A. "A Parasitic Fly on Horned Owls," *Oologist* (Vol. 51, 1934, pp. 4–5).

Stoddard, Herbert L., Sr. *Bird Casualties at a Leon County, Florida, TV Tower* (Bulletin #1). Tallahassee, Fla.: Tall Timbers Research Station, 1961.

Sutton, George M. "Does the Great Horned Owl Have a Poor Memory?" *Wilson Bulletin* (Vol. 41, 1929, pp. 247–248).

Terres, John K. "Great Horned Owls Dying in the Winter of 1939–40," *Auk* (Vol. 57, 1940, pp. 571–572).

Wilkinson, G. Norman. "Horned Owl Killing a Skunk," *Bird-Lore* (Vol. 15, 1913, p. 369).

INDEX

157

The World of the Great Horned Owl

  broken wing act, 75
  climbing to, 85–88
  defense of, by adults, 71–74
  searching for, 57–59, 61, 64–66

owl, species of:
  barn, 18
  barred, 25–26
  great gray, 15
  hawk, 19
  long-eared, 75, 145
  saw-whet, 144–145
  screech, 113–115, 135
  short-eared, 19
  snowy, 19
owls, as decoys, 45
  superstitions concerning, 147–148

Packard, Robt. L., 128–129
Payne, Roger S., 16, 18
pellets, 30, 32, 62, 135, 141–142, 144
photography, at nest, 92–111

range:
  home, 20–21, 140
  defense of, 22, 54
roost, 15, 20, 22–24, 32, 40, 63, 140–141, 145
  male's change in habits, 63–64
  male's, 61

saw-whet owl, 144–145

screech owl, 113–115, 135
short-eared owl, 19
skunk, 19
smell, sense of, 19
snowy owl, 19
starvation, 134
Stoddard, Herbert L., 134
subspecies, classification of, 150–152

traps, steel, 40–42
  Verbail, 42–43

vision, powers of, 13, 15–16, 136
voice, hunger squeals, 129
  response to imitations of, 37, 39–40

weight, 15
Wellfleet Audubon Sanctuary, 38
wingspread, 15
winter, 49

young:
  adults coaxing from nest, 112–113
  as pets, 107, 119–122, 130–132
  autumn drift, 140
  banding, 84
  dependency of, 49, 129
  first hunting attempts of, 117, 119
  growing self-sufficient, 117
  mortality of, 80–81, 83, 106
  nest leaving, 88–90, 92, 110, 116
  newly hatched, 76, 78
  parental separation, 133